"They'll take you away soon," Ginger said. "I'll lose my only friend. Most likely, we'll never see each other again. How cruel!"

About a week later Robert came into the field with a halter, slipped it over my head, and led me away. I didn't have a chance to really say goodbye to Ginger. We neighed to each other as I was led off, and she trotted anxiously along the hedge, calling to me as long as she could hear the sound of my feet.

A Background Note about *Black Beauty*

Set in London and other parts of southern England, *Black Beauty* tells the story of a horse born around 1860, before the existence of motor vehicles. Throughout England, people traveled by horseback and in horse-drawn vehicles such as carriages and cabs. Pulling carts, wagons, and vans, horses hauled goods and materials, from vegetables to bricks. Horses also regularly were used for sport, especially racing, pleasure riding, and hunting with hounds.

The abuses of horses described in *Black Beauty* were common. Horses routinely were beaten and whipped; forced to pull heavy loads; and worked when feeble, injured, or sick. On average, London cab horses gave out after only two years; many collapsed on the street. To reduce horse abuse, the Royal Society for the Prevention of Cruelty to Animals campaigned for better care and treatment of horses. *Black Beauty* significantly advanced that cause.

ANNA SEWELL

BLACK BEAUTY

The
Autobiography of a Horse

Edited, and with an Afterword,
by Joan Dunayer

 THE TOWNSEND LIBRARY

BLACK BEAUTY

TP THE TOWNSEND LIBRARY

For more titles in the Townsend Library,
visit our website: **www.townsendpress.com**

Townsend Press, Inc.
1038 Industrial Drive
West Berlin, New Jersey 08091

ISBN 1-59194-046-X

Library of Congress Control Number:
2005921078

CONTENTS

CHAPTER 1

My First Home

The first place that I remember well was a large, pleasant meadow with a clear pond. Some shady trees leaned over the pond; rushes and water lilies grew at its deep end. Looking over the hedge on one side of the meadow, we horses saw a plowed field. Looking over the hedge on the other side, we saw a gate at our master's house, which stood by the road. At the top of the meadow was a grove of fir trees; at the bottom, a running brook overhung by a steep bank.

When I was very young, I lived on my mother's milk. During the day, I ran by her side. At night I lay down beside her. When it was hot, we stood by the pond in the trees' shade. When it was cold, we stood in a nice warm shed near the grove. As soon as I was old enough to eat grass, my mother went to work during the day and came back each evening.

There were six colts in the meadow besides me. They were older than I was. Some were nearly as large as grown-up horses. I ran with them and had great fun. We galloped round and round the field as hard as we could. Sometimes we played roughly. Frequently the other colts playfully bit and kicked.

One day when there was much kicking, my mother whinnied to me to come to her. She said, "The colts who live here are good colts, but they're cart-horse colts, and they haven't learned good manners. You're a thoroughbred. Your father has a great name in these parts. Your grandfather won the Newmarket races twice. Your grandmother had the sweetest temper of any horse I ever knew. I never kick or bite. I hope you'll grow up gentle and good and never learn bad ways. Do your work willingly, lift your feet up well when you trot, and never bite or kick even in play."

I've never forgotten my mother's advice. I knew she was wise. Our master, Farmer Grey, thought a great deal of her. Her name was Duchess, but he often called her Pet.

Farmer Grey was a good, kind man. He gave us horses good food and good lodging. He spoke as kindly to us as he did to his little children. We all were fond of him. My mother loved him. Whenever she saw him at the gate, she'd neigh with joy and trot up to him. He'd pat and stroke her and say, "Well, old Pet, how's your little Darkie?" I was black, so he called me Darkie. Then he'd give me a piece of bread, which was very good. Sometimes he gave my mother a carrot. All of the horses would come to him, but I think my mother and I were his favorites. On market days, my mother always took Farmer Grey into town in a light carriage.

Sometimes a plowboy named Dick would come into our field to pluck blackberries from the hedge. When he'd eaten all that he wanted, he'd have what he called "fun" with the colts, throwing stones and sticks at us to make us gallop. We colts didn't mind him too much because we could gallop off, but sometimes a stone would hit and hurt us. One day while Dick was at his "fun," Farmer Grey was in the next field, watching. He jumped over the hedge and, catching Dick by the arm, gave him such a box on the ear that Dick roared with pain. We trotted up nearer to see what was happening. "Bad boy!" Farmer Grey said. "Bad boy to harass the colts! This isn't the first or second time, but it will be the last. There—take your money and go home. I don't want you on my farm again." We never saw Dick again.

Old Daniel, the man who looked after the horses, was as gentle as Farmer Grey, so we were well-off.

CHAPTER 2

The Hunt

Before I was two years old, something happened that I've never forgotten. It was early spring. There had been a light frost during the night. A fine mist hung over the woods and meadows. The other colts and I were feeding in the field's lower part when we heard the cry of dogs in the distance. The oldest colt raised his head, pricked his ears, said, "There are the hounds!" and cantered off. The rest of us followed him to the field's upper part, where we looked over the hedge and saw several fields beyond.

My mother and one of Farmer Grey's old riding horses were standing nearby and seemed to know what was happening. "They've found a hare," my mother said. "If they come this way, we'll see the hunt."

Soon all of the dogs were tearing down the field of young wheat next to ours. I'd never heard such a noise. They didn't bark, howl, or whine but loudly called, "Yoh! Yoh, oh!"

Men on horseback came after the dogs. Some of them wore green coats. They all galloped as fast as they could.

The old horse standing with my mother snorted and looked eagerly after the horses in the hunt. We young colts wanted to gallop with them. But they soon were in the fields lower down, where they halted. The dogs stopped barking and ran here and there with their noses to the ground.

"They've lost the scent," the old horse said. "Maybe the hare will get away."

"What hare?" I asked.

"I don't know what hare. Any hare they can find will do for the dogs and men to run after."

Before long the dogs cried "Yoh! Yoh, oh!" again. They all came back at full speed, making straight for our meadow, where the high bank and hedge overhung the brook.

"Now we'll see the hare," my mother said.

Wild with fear, a hare rushed by and made for the woods.

The dogs pursued. They burst over the bank, leaped the stream, and came dashing across the field followed by the huntsmen. Six or eight men leaped their horses clean over, close upon the dogs.

The hare tried to get through the fence, but

she couldn't find a big enough opening. She turned around sharply to make for the road. Too late. The dogs were on her with their wild cries. We heard one shriek, and that was the end of her.

One of the huntsmen rode up and whipped off the dogs, who would have torn the dead hare to pieces. He held up the hare's body, torn and bleeding, by one leg. All the men seemed pleased.

I was so astonished that at first I didn't see what was happening by the brook. When I looked, there was a sad sight. Two fine horses were down. One was struggling in the stream. The other was groaning on the grass. One of the riders was getting out of the water covered with mud. The other, a young man, lay motionless.

"That rider's neck is broken," my mother said.

"Serves him right," one of the colts said.

I thought the same.

My mother said, "I don't know why people like this sport. They tear up the fields, often hurt themselves, often cause the death of good horses—all to kill some poor hare, fox, or deer."

While my mother was saying this, we stood and looked on. Many of the riders had gone to the motionless young man. Farmer Grey, who had been watching what was happening, was the first to lift him. The young man's head fell back;

his arms hung down. Everyone looked very serious. There was no noise now. Even the dogs were quiet and seemed to know that something was wrong.

People carried the young man to Farmer Grey's house. I heard afterward that it was young George Gordon, Squire Gordon's only son, a fine, tall young man and the pride of his family.

Men now rode off in all directions—to the physician, to the horse doctor, and no doubt to Squire Gordon, to let him know about his son.

When Mr. Bond, the horse doctor, came to look at the black horse who lay groaning on the grass, he shook his head. One of the horse's legs was broken. Someone ran to Farmer Grey's house and came back with a gun. Presently there was a loud bang and a dreadful shriek. Then all was still. The black horse moved no more.

My mother was very upset. She said that the horse's name was Rob Roy and that he was a fine horse with no vices. After that, she never would go to that part of the field.

A few days later the church bell tolled for a long time. Looking over the gate, we saw a long black coach covered with black cloth and drawn by black horses. Other black coaches followed. The bell kept tolling. Young George Gordon was being brought to the churchyard for burial. I never learned what they did with Rob Roy. All this to terrify and kill one little hare.

CHAPTER 3

My Breaking In

I began to grow handsome. My coat was fine, soft, and bright black. I had one white foot and a pretty white star on my forehead. Farmer Grey wouldn't sell me until I was four years old. He said that boys shouldn't work like men, and colts shouldn't work like grown-up horses.

When I was four, Squire Gordon came to look at me. He examined my eyes, mouth, and legs, which he felt. I had to walk, trot, and gallop in front of him. He seemed to like me. He said, "When he's been broken in, he'll do very well."

Farmer Grey said that he'd break me in himself because he didn't want me to be frightened or hurt. He began the next day.

To "break" horses means to teach them to wear a saddle and bridle, carry people on their back, go just as the rider wishes, and go quietly.

In addition, horses must learn to wear a collar and straps and to stand still while they're put on. They also must learn to have a cart or carriage attached behind them, so that they can't walk or trot without dragging it after them. They must go fast or slow, as their driver wishes. They mustn't ever start at what they see, speak to other horses, bite, kick, or have any will of their own. They must always do what their master or mistress wishes, even though they may be very tired or hungry. Worst of all, when their harness is on, they may neither jump for joy nor lie down from weariness.

I was used to wearing a halter and headstall and to being quietly led about in the fields and lanes. But now I was to have a bit and bridle. Farmer Grey gave me some oats as usual. After much coaxing he got the bit into my mouth and the bridle fixed. The bit was a nasty thing! Those who never have had a bit in their mouth can't imagine how bad it feels. A great piece of cold, hard steel as thick as a man's finger is pushed into your mouth, between your teeth, and over your tongue. The ends come out at the corners of your mouth and are held fast by straps over your head, under your throat, around your nose, and under your chin. There's no way that you can get rid of the nasty, hard thing. It's very bad. I knew that my mother always wore a bit when she went out and that all horses wore one when they were grown up. That knowledge, combined with the nice oats and Farmer Grey's pats, kind words, and gentle ways, persuaded me to accept the bit and bridle.

Next came the saddle. That wasn't half as bad. Farmer Grey put it on my back very gently while old Daniel held my head. Farmer Grey then fastened the girths under my body, patting and talking to me the whole time. Then I had a few oats, then a little leading about. Farmer Grey did this every day until I began to look for the oats and the saddle.

Finally, one morning Farmer Grey got on my back and rode me around the meadow on the soft grass. It felt strange, but I was rather proud to carry my master. He continued to ride me a little each day, and I soon became accustomed to it.

The next unpleasant business was wearing iron shoes. That, too, was very hard at first. Farmer Grey went with me to the blacksmith, to see that I wasn't hurt or frightened. The blacksmith took my feet in his hand, one after the other, and cut away some of the hoof. It didn't hurt, so I stood still on three legs until he'd done every foot. Then he took a piece of iron the shape of my foot, clapped it on, and drove some nails through the shoe and into my hoof, so that the shoe was firmly on. My feet felt very stiff and heavy, but I got used to it after a while.

Next, Farmer Grey broke me to harness. There were more new things to wear: a stiff, heavy collar on my neck; a bridle with great side-pieces against my eyes called blinders, which prevented me from seeing anywhere except straight in front of me; and a small saddle with a crupper, a nasty, stiff strap that went under my tail. I hated the crupper. Having my long tail doubled up and poked through that strap was almost as bad as wearing the bit. I never felt more like kicking. But I couldn't kick such a good master, so in time I got used to everything and did my work as well as my mother.

I mustn't forget to mention one part of my training that I've always considered a great advantage. Farmer Grey sent me for two weeks to a neighboring farm that had a meadow skirted on one side by a railway. There were some sheep and cows, and I was turned in among them.

I'll never forget the first train that ran by. I was quietly feeding near the fencing that separated the meadow from the railway when I heard a strange sound at a distance. Before I knew where it came from, a long, black train flew by, with a rush, clatter, and puffing out of smoke. It was gone almost before I could draw my breath. I turned and galloped to the meadow's far side as fast as I could. I stood there snorting with astonishment and fear.

During the day many other trains went by. The slower ones drew up at the nearby station and sometimes made an awful shriek and groan before they stopped. I thought the noise was dreadful. But the cows went on eating quietly and hardly raised their heads as the black, frightful thing came puffing and grinding past.

For the first few days I couldn't eat in peace. But when I realized that this huge machine never came into the field or harmed me, I began to disregard it. Soon I cared as little about a train's passing as the cows and sheep did.

Since then I've seen many horses become greatly alarmed at the sight or sound of a steam engine. Thanks to Farmer Grey's care, I'm as fearless at railway stations as in my own stable.

If anyone wants to break in a young horse well, that's the way.

Farmer Grey often drove me in double harness with my mother because she was steady and could show me how to go. My mother told me that the better I behaved, the better I'd be treated, and that it was wise always to do my best to please my master or mistress. "But," she said, "there are many kinds of people. There are good, thoughtful people, like our master, whom any horse would be proud to serve, and there are bad, cruel people, who never should own a horse. Also, there are many foolish people— vain, ignorant, and careless—who never think.

These people ruin many horses because they lack good sense. They don't mean to, but they do. I hope you'll fall into good hands. But horses never know who might buy or drive them. Wherever you are, do your best. Keep up your good name."

CHAPTER 4

Birtwick Park

In early May a man came to take me away to Squire Gordon's home, Birtwick Park.

Farmer Grey said, "Goodbye, Darkie. Be a good horse. Always do your best."

I couldn't say goodbye, so I put my nose into his hand.

He patted me kindly, and I left my first home.

Squire Gordon's park skirted the village of Birtwick. At the park's entrance was a large iron gate, where the first lodge stood. Then there was a smooth road between clumps of large, old trees. After another lodge and gate were the house and gardens. Beyond these were the home paddock, old orchard, and stables. There was accommodation for many horses and carriages.

The stable to which I was taken was roomy. It had four good stalls. A large swinging window opened into the yard, making the stable pleasant and airy.

The first stall was a large square one shut with a wooden gate. The others were common stalls, good but not nearly as large. The first stall had a corn manger and low hay rack. It was a loose stall, in which a horse isn't tied but is left loose to do as they like. It's a great thing to have a loose stall. The groom put me into this fine stall. It was clean, sweet, and airy. I never was in a better stall. The sides were low enough that, through the iron rails at the top, I could see everything that happened.

The groom gave me some good oats, patted me, spoke kindly, and went away. When I'd eaten my corn, I looked around.

In the stall next to mine stood a chubby, little gray pony with a thick mane and tail, a pretty head, and a pert little nose. I put my head up to the iron rails at the top of my stall and said, "How do you do? What's your name?"

He turned around as far as his halter would allow, held up his head, and said, "I'm Merrylegs. I'm very handsome. I carry the young ladies—Flora and Jessie—on my back. Sometimes I take our mistress out in a low chair on wheels. The ladies think a great deal of me. So does James. Are you going to live next door to me in the loose stall?"

"Yes."

"Well, then," he said, "I hope you're good-tempered. I don't like having anyone next door who bites."

Just then a horse's head looked over from the stall beyond. The ears were laid back. The eyes looked rather ill-tempered. This was a tall chestnut mare with a long, handsome neck. She looked over at me and said, "So you're the one who has turned me out of my stall. It's a strange thing for a colt like you to come and turn a lady out of her home."

"I beg your pardon," I said. "I haven't turned anyone out. The man who brought me put me here. I had nothing to do with it. As for my being a colt, I'm four years old, a grown-up horse. I've never argued with any horse, and I don't want to. I hope to live in peace."

"Well," she said, "we'll see. I don't want to argue with a young thing like you."

In the afternoon, when she went out, Merrylegs told me about her. "Ginger has a bad habit of biting and snapping. When she was in the loose stall, she snapped a lot. One day she bit James in his arm and made it bleed, so Flora and Jessie, who are very fond of me, were afraid to come into the stable. They used to bring me nice things to eat—an apple, a carrot, or a piece of bread—but when Ginger was in that stall, they didn't dare come in. I missed them very much. I hope they'll come again now, if you don't bite or snap."

"I never bite anything but grass, hay, or corn," I said. "I don't know what pleasure Ginger finds in biting people."

"I don't think she finds pleasure in it," Merrylegs said. "It's just a bad habit. She says that no one ever was kind to her, so why shouldn't she bite? If everything that she says is true, she was badly abused before she came here. John and James do everything they can to please her, and our master never uses a whip if a horse behaves properly, so I think she might be good-tempered here. You see," he said with a wise look, "I'm twelve years old. I know a great deal. I can tell you that there's no better place for a horse in all of England than here. John is the best groom ever. He's been here fourteen years. And you never saw a kinder boy than James. So it's Ginger's own fault that she didn't stay in that stall."

CHAPTER 5

A Fair Start

The coachman was John Manly. He had a wife and one little child, and they lived in the coachman's cottage, very near the stables. The next morning he took me into the yard and gave me a good grooming.

Just as I was going into my stall, with my coat soft and bright, Squire Gordon came in to look at me. He seemed pleased. "John," he said, "I meant to try the new horse this morning, but I have other business. Take him around after breakfast. Go by way of the common and woods, and come back by the watermill and river. That will show his paces."

"I will, sir," John said.

After breakfast John came and fitted me with a bridle. He was very particular about letting out and taking in the straps so that the bridle fit my head comfortably. Then he brought a saddle, but it wasn't broad enough for my back.

He saw this in a minute and went for another, which fitted nicely. He rode me first slowly, then at a trot, then at a canter. When we were on the common, he gave me a light touch with his whip, and we had a splendid gallop.

"Ho! Ho, my boy," he said as he pulled me up. "You'd like to follow the hounds, I think."

As we came back through the park, we met Squire and Mrs. Gordon walking. They stopped, and John jumped off.

"Well, John, how did he do?"

"He's first-rate, sir," John answered. "He's as fleet as a deer, and he has a fine spirit. The lightest touch of the rein is enough to guide him. Down at the end of the common, we came across one of those traveling carts hung all over with baskets, rugs, and such. Many horses won't pass those carts quietly. He just took a good look at it and then went on as quiet and pleasant as could be. They were shooting rabbits near the woods, and a gun went off close by. He pulled up a little and looked but didn't stir a step to the right or left. I held the rein steady and didn't hurry him. It's my opinion that he hasn't ever been abused."

"Good," Squire Gordon said. "I'll try him myself tomorrow."

The next day I was brought up for Squire Gordon. I remembered the advice of my mother and Farmer Grey. I tried to do exactly what

Squire Gordon wanted me to do. I found he was a very good rider and thoughtful toward his horse.

When Squire Gordon came home, Mrs. Gordon was at the hall door as he rode up. "Well, my dear," she said, "how do you like him?"

"He's exactly what John said," Squire Gordon replied. "I don't expect to ever ride a more pleasant creature. What shall we call him?"

"How about Ebony? He's as black as ebony."

"No, not Ebony," Squire Gordon said.

"We could call him Blackbird, after your uncle's old horse."

"No. He's much handsomer than Blackbird ever was."

"Yes," she said, "he really is a beauty. And he has such a sweet, good-tempered face and such fine, intelligent eyes. Why don't we call him Black Beauty?"

"Black Beauty. Yes. I think that's a very good name."

When John went into the stable, he told James Howard, the stable boy, that master and mistress had given me a good, sensible English name that meant something, not a foreign name like Pegasus or Abdullah. They both laughed.

James said, "If it wasn't for bringing back the past, I would have named him Rob Roy because I never saw two horses more alike."

"That's no wonder," John said. "Farmer Grey's old Duchess was the mother of both of them."

I'd never heard that before. So, poor Rob Roy who was killed at that hunt was my brother! No wonder my mother had been so upset. People act as if horses have no family, but of course we do, even though we're often separated from our kin when one of us is sold.

John seemed proud of me. He'd make my mane and tail as smooth as a lady's hair, and he'd talk to me a lot. I usually knew what he meant and what he wanted me to do. I grew very fond of him. He was gentle and kind. He seemed to know just how a horse feels. When he cleaned me, he knew the tender and ticklish places. When he brushed my head, he went as carefully over my eyes as if they were his own and never made me feel ill-tempered.

James also was gentle and pleasant, so I considered myself well-off. Another man helped in the yard, but he had very little to do with Ginger and me.

A few days later, I had to go out with Ginger in the carriage. I wondered how we'd get on together. Except that she laid her ears back when I was led up to her, she behaved very well. She did her work honestly and did her full share, and I don't expect to ever have a better partner in double harness. Whenever we came to a hill, instead of slackening her pace she'd throw her weight into the collar and pull straight up. We both worked hard. John had to hold us in more often than urge us forward. He never had to use the whip on either of us. Our paces were much the same. I found it easy to keep step with Ginger when trotting, which was pleasant. Squire Gordon always liked it when we kept step well. So did John. After we'd been out together two or three times, Ginger and I became quite friendly, which made me feel very much at home.

Merrylegs and I soon became great friends. He was such a cheerful, plucky, good-tempered little fellow that he was a favorite with everyone, especially Jessie and Flora, who would ride him around the orchard and play games with him and their little dog Frisky.

Squire Gordon had two other horses who stood in another stable. One was Justice, a roan cob used for riding or for the luggage cart. The other was an old brown hunter named Sir Oliver. He was past work now but was a great favorite with Squire Gordon, who gave him the run of the park. Sir Oliver sometimes did a little light carting on the estate. Also, because he was very gentle and, like Merrylegs, could be trusted with a child, he sometimes carried one of the young ladies when they rode out with their father. Sir Oliver was strong, well-built, and good-tempered. We sometimes chatted in the paddock. But I couldn't be as intimate with him as with Ginger, who was housed in the same stable as I was.

CHAPTER 6

Liberty

Overall I was happy in my new place. Everyone who dealt with me was good. I had a light, airy stable and the best food. What more could I want? Liberty!

For three and a half years of my life, I'd had all the liberty I wanted. Now, week after week, month after month, I had to stand in a stable day and night except when I was wanted, and then I had to be as steady and quiet as an old horse who has worked twenty years. Straps here and straps there. A bit in my mouth. Blinders over my eyes. For young, strong, spirited horses who are used to a large field or plain where they can fling up their head, toss their tail, and gallop at full speed, then around and back again with a snort to their companions, it's hard to have little liberty.

Sometimes, when I'd had less exercise than usual, I felt so full of life and spring that when

John took me out to exercise, I couldn't stay quiet. I had to jump, dance, or prance. I must have given John many a good shake, especially at first, but he always was good and patient.

"Steady, boy, steady," he'd say. "Wait a bit, and we'll have a good swing and get the tickle out of your feet." As soon as we were out of the village, he'd give me a few miles at a good trot and then bring me back feeling fresh, no longer fidgety.

Spirited horses who don't get enough exercise often are skittish. Some grooms punish them, but John didn't. He knew it was only high spirits. When he was very serious and determined, I knew it from the tone of his voice. That had more power with me than anything else because I was very fond of him.

On fine Sundays during the summer, we horses sometimes had liberty for a few hours. The carriage never went out on Sundays because the church was nearby. We horses considered it a great treat to be turned out into the home paddock or the old orchard. The grass was cool and soft to our feet, the air was sweet, and the freedom to do as we liked was wonderful. We could gallop, lie down, roll over on our backs, or nibble the sweet grass. It was a good time for talking, as we stood together under the shade of the large chestnut tree.

CHAPTER 7

Ginger

One day when Ginger and I were standing alone in the shade, we talked a lot. She wanted to know all about my upbringing and breaking in, and I told her.

"Well," she said, "if I'd had your upbringing, I might have had as good a temper as you. Now I don't think I ever will."

"Why not?" I asked.

"It's all been so different for me," she replied. "There never was anyone—horse or human—who was kind to me or whom I cared to please. I was taken from my mother as soon as I was weaned and put with many other young colts. None of them cared for me, and I didn't care for any of them. There was no kind master like your Farmer Grey to look after me, talk to me, and bring me nice things to eat. The man charged with caring for us colts never gave me a kind word. He didn't abuse me, but he didn't care for us one bit more than to see that we had plenty to eat and shelter in the winter.

"A footpath ran through our field. Often, adolescent boys passing through would fling stones to make us gallop. I never was hit, but one fine young colt was badly cut in the face, scarred for life. Of course, the stone throwing made us more wild. We decided that boys were our enemies.

"We had fun in the meadows. We galloped up and down, chased one another around the field, and stood under the trees. But breaking in was a bad time for me. Several men came to catch me. When they finally closed me in at one corner of the field, one grabbed me by the fore-lock, another grabbed me by the nose and held it so tight that I hardly could breathe, and another took my lower jaw in his hard hand and wrenched my mouth open. By force they got the halter on and the bar into my mouth. Then one dragged me along by the halter, another flogging behind. This was my first experience of people. It was all force. They didn't even give me a chance to know what they wanted.

"I was thoroughbred and high-spirited and, no doubt, very wild. I dare say I gave them plenty of trouble, but it was dreadful to be shut up in a stall day after day instead of having liberty. I fretted and pined and wanted to get loose. It's bad enough when you have a kind master or mistress and plenty of coaxing. There was nothing of that sort for me.

"There was one person—the old master, Mr. Ryder—who, I think, could have quickly brought me around and done anything with me. But he had turned over the hard part of the trade to his son and another man, so he came only at times, to oversee. His son was a strong, tall, bold man named Samson. He boasted that he'd never found a horse who could throw him. There was no gentleness in him, only hardness. He had a hard voice, a hard eye, and a hard hand. From the beginning I felt that he wanted to crush my spirit and turn me into a quiet, humble, obedient piece of horseflesh. Horseflesh! Yes, that's all he thought about."

Ginger angrily stamped her foot. "If I didn't do exactly as he wanted, he'd get angry and make me run around in the training field until he'd exhausted me. He drank a lot. The more he drank, the worse it was for me. One day, he worked me hard in every way that he could. When I lay down, I was tired, miserable, and angry. The next morning he came for me early and ran me around again for a long time. I'd scarcely had an hour's rest when he came for me again, with a saddle, bridle, and new kind of bit. He'd only just mounted me on the training ground when something I did put him out of temper. He jerked me hard with the rein. The new bit was very painful. I reared up suddenly, which made him even angrier, and he began to flog me. My whole spirit set against him. I kicked, plunged, and reared as never before. For a long time he stuck to the saddle and punished me cruelly with his whip and spurs. I was determined to throw him. Finally, after a terrible struggle, I threw him off backward. I heard him fall heavily onto the turf. Without looking behind me, I galloped off to the other end of the field. There I turned around and saw my persecutor slowly rising from the ground and going into the stable.

"I stood under an oak tree and watched, but no one came to fetch me. Time passed. The sun was very hot. Flies swarmed around me and settled on my bleeding flanks where the spurs had dug in. I was hungry. I hadn't eaten since early in the morning, but there wasn't enough grass in that meadow for a goose. I wanted to lie down and rest, but with the saddle strapped tightly on, there was no comfort and there wasn't a drop of water to drink. The afternoon wore on, and the sun got low. I saw the other colts be led in, and I knew they were having a good meal.

"At last, at sunset Mr. Ryder came out with a sieve in his hand. He was a fine old gentleman with white hair. His voice was full, clear, and kind. When he gave orders, his voice was so steady and decided that everyone—horses and humans—knew that he expected to be obeyed. He came quietly toward me, now and then shaking the oats in the sieve and speaking to me cheerfully and gently. 'Come along, girl. Come along.' I stood still and let him come up. Mr. Ryder held the oats to me, and I began to eat without fear. His voice took all my fear away. He stood by, patting and stroking me while I ate. Seeing the clots of blood on my side, he seemed very upset. 'Poor girl! It was a bad business.'

"Mr. Ryder quietly took the rein and led me to the stable. Samson stood at the door. I laid my ears back and snapped at him. 'Stand back,' Mr. Ryder said to his son, 'and keep out of her way. You've been a vicious brute and done a bad day's work with this filly. A bad-tempered man never produces a good-tempered horse. You haven't learned your trade.'

"Mr. Ryder led me into my stall, removed my saddle and bridle, and tied me up. Then he called for a pail of warm water and a sponge, took off his coat, and, while the stableman held the pail, sponged my sides so tenderly that I was sure he knew how wounded they were. 'Whoa, pretty one,' he said. 'Stand still.' His voice did me good, and the bathing was very comfortable. The skin at the corners of my mouth was so broken that I couldn't eat the hay; the stalks hurt me. Mr. Ryder looked closely at the hay, shook his head, and told the stableman to fetch a good bran mash and put some meal into it. That mash was very good, and very soft and healing to my mouth. Mr. Ryder stood by all the time that I was eating, stroking me and talking to the stableman. 'If a high-spirited creature like this can't be broken by fair means, she won't ever be good for anything.'

"After that, Mr. Ryder often came to see me. When my mouth was healed, the other breaker continued my training. He was steady and thoughtful, so I soon learned what he wanted."

CHAPTER 8

Ginger's Story
Continued

The next time that Ginger and I were together in the paddock, she told me about her first place. She said, "After my breaking in, a dealer bought me to match another chestnut horse. He drove us together for some weeks. Then we were sold to a fashionable gentleman and sent up to London. The dealer had driven me with a checkrein, which I hated worse than anything else. But in this place we were reined much tighter. The coachman and his master thought we looked more stylish that way. We often were driven about in the park and other fashionable places. You've never had a checkrein on, so you don't know what it's like. It's dreadful. It pulls your head up high and prevents you from lowering it. I like to toss my head about and hold it as high as any horse, but imagine if you tossed your head up high and had to hold it there for hours, your neck aching until you didn't know how to bear it. Besides the checkrein, I had two bits instead of one, and they were sharp. They hurt my tongue and jaw. The blood from my tongue colored the froth that kept flying from my lips as the bits and checkrein tormented me. It was worst when we had to stand waiting, for hours, while our mistress was at some grand party or other entertainment. If I fretted or stamped with impatience, I was whipped."

"Didn't your master consider your feelings at all?" I asked.

"No. He cared only about looking stylish. I think he knew very little about horses. He left my treatment to his coachman, who told him that I was irritable, that I hadn't been well broken to the checkrein, and that I'd soon get used to it. When I was in the stable, miserable and angry, instead of quieting and soothing me with kindness, the coachman would give me a surly word or a blow. If he'd been kind, I'd have tried to bear it. I was willing to work hard, but to be tormented for nothing but fashion angered me. What right did they have to make me suffer like that? Besides making my mouth sore and causing pain in my neck, the checkrein always hurt my windpipe. If I'd stayed there a long time, it would have damaged my breathing.

"I became more restless and irritable. I couldn't help it. I began to snap and kick when anyone came to harness me. The groom beat me for this. One day, right after they buckled us into the carriage and strained my head up with the checkrein, I plunged and kicked with all my might. I broke my harness and kicked myself clear. After that I was sent to Tattersall's to be sold.

"A dealer bought me because of my handsome appearance and good paces. He tried me in all kinds of ways and with different bits, and he soon found what I couldn't bear. At last he drove me without a checkrein. Then he sold me as a perfectly quiet horse to a country gentleman.

"This gentleman was a good master. I got on well until his old groom left and a new one came. The new groom was as hard-tempered and hard-handed as Samson. He always spoke in a rough, impatient voice. If I didn't move in the stall the moment he wanted me to, he'd hit me above my ankle with a broom or pitchfork, whichever he had in his hand. Everything he did was rough. I started to hate him. He wanted me to fear him, but I was too high-spirited for that. One day when he'd aggravated me more than usual, I bit him. This enraged him. He hit me about the head with a riding whip. After that he never again dared to enter my stall. My heels or teeth always were ready for him, and he knew that. I was quiet with my master, but he listened to the groom, so I was offered for sale again.

"The same dealer heard about me and said he knew of a place where he thought I'd do well. 'It's a pity for such a fine horse to go bad because she hasn't had a good chance,' he said. I came here not long before you did. By then I'd decided that humans were my enemies and I must defend myself against them. It's very different here, but who knows how long it will last? I wish I could think about things as you do, but I can't, not after all I've been through."

"Well," I said, "I think it would be a real shame if you bit or kicked John or James."

"I don't plan to if they continue to be good to me. I gave James a sharp bite once. John said, 'Be kind to her.' Instead of punishing me as I'd expected, James came to me with his arm bound up and brought me a bran mash and stroked me. I haven't snapped at him since."

I felt sorry for Ginger. As the weeks passed, she grew much more gentle and cheerful. She lost the watchful, defiant look that she previously had turned on any stranger who came near her.

One day James said, "I believe that mare is getting fond of me. She whinnied after me this morning when I'd been rubbing her forehead."

"Yes, Jim," John said. "She'll soon be as good as Black Beauty. Kindness is all that she needs, poor thing."

Squire Gordon noticed the change, too. One day when he got out of the carriage and came to speak to us, as he often did, he stroked Ginger's beautiful neck. "Well, my pretty one, how are you now? You're much happier than when you came to us, I think."

Ginger put her nose up to him in a friendly, trusting way while he rubbed it gently.

"We'll cure her, John," Squire Gordon said.

"Yes, sir. She's greatly improved. She's not the same creature that she was."

CHAPTER 9

Merrylegs

Mr. Blomefield, the vicar, had a large family of boys and girls. Sometimes they'd come and play with Jessie and Flora. One of the vicar's daughters was the same age as Jessie, two of the boys were older, and there were several little ones. When the vicar's children came, there was plenty of work for Merrylegs. Nothing pleased the children more than getting on him by turns and riding him all about the orchard and the home paddock for hours.

One afternoon Merrylegs was out with the children a long time. After bringing Merrylegs in and putting his halter on him, James said, "There, you rogue. Mind how you behave, or we'll get into trouble."

"What have you been doing, Merrylegs?" I asked.

"Oh!" he said, tossing his little head. "I've only been giving those children a lesson. They didn't know when I'd had enough, so I pitched them off backward. That was the only thing they could understand."

"What? You threw the children off? I thought you knew better than that! You threw Jessie and Flora?"

Merrylegs looked offended. "Of course not. I wouldn't do that for the best oats that ever came into the stable. I'm as careful with our young ladies as Squire Gordon would be. I'm the one who teaches them to ride. When they seem frightened or a little unsteady on my back, I go as smoothly and quietly as a cat after a bird. When they're steady, I go more quickly, to get them used to it. I'm the best friend and best riding teacher Jessie and Flora could have. It isn't them. It's the vicar's boys. Boys," he said, shaking his mane, "are quite different from girls. They must be broken in as we were broken in when we were colts. They must be taught what's what. The other children had ridden me for nearly two hours. Then the boys thought it was their turn. So it was, and I was agreeable. They rode me by turns, and I galloped them about, up and down the fields and all about the orchard, for a good hour. They each had cut a large hazel stick to use as a riding whip, and they laid it on a little too hard. I took it in good part until I finally decided that I'd had enough. I stopped two or three times as a hint. Boys think a pony is like a steam engine and can go as long and fast as they please. They don't think that a pony can get tired or have any feelings. So, because the one who was whipping me couldn't understand, I rose up on my hind legs and let him slip off behind. He mounted me again, and I did the same. Then the other boy got on me. As soon as he began to use his stick, I laid him on the grass. I had to teach those boys a lesson. When they brought me to James and told him, I think he was very angry to see such big sticks. He said they were unfit for gentlemen."

"If I'd been you," Ginger said, "I'd have given those boys a good kick. That would have taught them a lesson."

"No doubt you would," Merrylegs said, "but I'm not foolish enough—begging your pardon—to anger Squire Gordon or make James ashamed of me. Besides, those children are under my charge when they're riding; they're entrusted to me. Just the other day I heard Squire Gordon say to Mrs. Blomefield, 'My dear madam, you needn't be anxious about your children. My old Merrylegs will take as much care of them as you or I would. He's perfectly good-tempered and trustworthy.' Do you think I'm so ungrateful that I'd forget all the kind treatment I've received here for five years, and all the trust they place in me, and turn vicious because a couple of ignorant boys abused me? No! You never had a good place where people were kind to you, so you don't know, and I'm sorry for you. Good places make good horses. I wouldn't upset our people for anything. I love them."

Merrylegs gave a low "ho, ho" through his nose, as he did each morning when he heard James's footsteps at the door. "Besides, if I took to kicking, where would I be? Why, sold off in a jiffy and not recommended as being of good character. I might find myself the slave of some butcher's boy who hurries to and fro. Or I might be worked to death at some seaside place where no one cared about me except to find out how fast I could go. I might be flogged along in some cart with three or four large men in it going out for a Sunday spree, as I often saw in the place where I lived before I came here. No," he said, shaking his head, "I hope I never come to that."

CHAPTER 10

A Talk in the Orchard

Ginger and I weren't of the regular, tall carriage-horse breed. We had more racing blood in us. We stood about fifteen and a half hands high. Therefore, we were just as good for riding as for driving. Ginger and I took great pleasure in being saddled for a riding party—Squire Gordon on Ginger, Mrs. Gordon on me, Jessie on Sir Oliver, and Flora on Merrylegs. It was so cheerful to trot and canter together that it always put us in high spirits. I had the best of it because I always carried the mistress. She didn't weigh much, her voice was sweet, and her hand was so light on the rein that I was guided almost without feeling it.

If people knew what a comfort to horses a light hand is and how it results in a horse's having a good temper and not biting, they wouldn't jerk and pull the rein as they often do. A horse's mouth is very tender. When our mouth hasn't been hardened with cruel or ignorant treatment, we feel the slightest movement of the driver's hand; we instantly know what's required of us. My mouth wasn't spoiled. I think that's why Mrs. Gordon preferred me to Ginger, whose paces were as good as mine.

Ginger envied me. She said that her mouth wasn't as perfect as mine because of the way she'd been broken in and the gag bit that she'd been forced to wear in London.

Old Sir Oliver would say, "There, there! Don't upset yourself. You have the greatest honor. A mare who can carry a tall man of our master's weight with all your spring and sprightly action shouldn't feel ashamed because she doesn't carry the lady. We horses must take things as they come and be willing and content as long as we're treated kindly."

I'd often wondered why Sir Oliver had such a short tail, only about six inches long, with a tassel of hair hanging from it. On one of our holidays in the orchard, I asked him, "What accident caused you to lose your tail?"

"Accident?" he snorted with a fierce look. "It wasn't an accident. It was a cruel, shameful, cold-blooded act. When I was young, I was taken to a place where tails were cut short. I was tied up so that I couldn't move. Then they cut off my long, beautiful tail—right through the flesh and bone."

"How dreadful!" I exclaimed.

"Yes, it *was* dreadful. The pain was terrible and lasted a long time. I also suffered the indignity of having my best ornament taken from me. Worst of all, I couldn't brush the flies off my sides and hind legs anymore. Horses with full tails whisk flies off without thinking about it. You don't know what a torment it is to have flies settle on you and sting and sting, and you have nothing to lash them off with. It's a lifelong wrong and a lifelong loss. Thank heaven, they don't do it anymore."

"Why did they do it *then*?" Ginger asked.

"For fashion!" the old horse said with an angry stamp of his foot. "In my time, all young thoroughbreds had their tails cut short in that shameful way, as if God who made us didn't know what we need and what looks best."

"I suppose it's fashion that makes people strap our heads up with those horrid bits that I was tortured with in London," Ginger said.

"Of course it is," Sir Oliver said. "Fashion is one of the wickedest things in the world. Look at the way they treat dogs, cutting off most of their tail and cropping their ears so that they stand up straight and come to a point. I had a dear friend once, a brown terrier called Skye. She was so fond of me that she never would sleep outside my stall. She made her bed under the manger and had a litter of five pretty puppies there. None of them was drowned because they were valuable. Skye was so pleased with them! When they opened their eyes and crawled around, it was a pretty sight. One day a man came and took them all away. In the evening poor Skye brought them back, one by one, in her mouth. They no longer were happy. Instead they were bleeding and crying pitifully. They'd all had most of their tail cut off, and the soft flap of their little ears. How their mother licked them, and how troubled she was, poor thing! I've never forgotten it. The puppies healed in time, and they forgot the pain, but the nice soft flap that would have protected the delicate part of their ears from dust and injury was gone forever. Why don't humans cut their children's ears into points to make them look sharp? That would make as much sense as mutilating horses or dogs. What right do humans have to torment and disfigure us?"

Sir Oliver, though gentle, was a fiery old fellow. What he said was so new to me, and so dreadful, that I felt a new bitterness toward humans.

Ginger, too, was indignant. With flashing eyes and distended nostrils, she flung up her head, declaring, "Humans are brutes and blockheads."

"'Blockheads' is a bad word," Merrylegs said as he came up from the old apple tree, where he'd been rubbing himself against the lowest branch.

"Bad words are appropriate for bad things," Ginger said, and she told him what Sir Oliver had said.

"It's all true," Merrylegs said sadly. "In my first home I saw many dogs treated like that. But we shouldn't talk about it here. Squire Gordon, John, and James always are good to us. Speaking against humans in a place like this doesn't seem fair or grateful. Besides, there are good masters and grooms other than ours, although ours are the best."

This wise speech of good little Merrylegs cooled us down, especially Sir Oliver, who was dearly fond of Squire Gordon.

To change the subject, I said, "Can anyone tell me the reason that blinders are used?"

"No," Sir Oliver said shortly, "because there isn't any reason."

In his calm way, Justice the roan cob said, "They're supposed to prevent horses from shying, starting, and getting so frightened that they cause accidents."

"Then, why don't they put them on riding horses, especially ladies' horses?" I asked.

"There's no real reason for blinders except fashion," Justice said quietly. "They say that horses would be so frightened to see the wheels of their own cart or carriage coming behind them that they'd run away. However, when they're ridden, they see cart and carriage wheels all around them if the streets are crowded. The wheels sometimes come unpleasantly close, but we don't run away. We're used to it and understand it. If we never had blinders on, we never would want them. We'd see what's there and know what's what and be much less frightened than by seeing only parts of things that we can't understand."

"I think blinders are dangerous at night," Sir Oliver said. "We horses can see much better in the dark than humans can. Many accidents never would have happened if horses had been permitted the full use of their eyes. One dark night some years ago, a hearse with two horses was returning near Farmer Sparrow's house. Where the pond is close to the road, the wheels of the hearse went too near the edge. The hearse overturned into the water. Both of the horses drowned, and the driver barely escaped. After this accident a sturdy white rail was put up. If those horses hadn't been partly blinded, they would have stayed farther from the edge, and no accident would have occurred. When Squire Gordon's carriage overturned, before you came here, it was said that if the lamp on the left side hadn't gone out, John would have seen the large hole left by the road-makers. That may be true, but if old Colin hadn't had blinders on, he would have seen the hole, lamp or no lamp. As it was, he was badly hurt, the carriage was broken, and John was lucky to escape serious injury."

Curling her nostrils, Ginger said, "If humans are so wise, they should give orders that all foals be born with their eyes in the middle of their forehead instead of on the side. Humans always think they can improve on nature."

Seeing that things were heating up again, Merrylegs held up his knowing little face and said, "John disapproves of blinders. I heard him talking with Squire Gordon about it one day. Squire Gordon said, 'If horses are used to them, it might be dangerous to leave them off.' John said he thought all colts should be broken in without blinders. So let's cheer up and have a run to the other end of the orchard. I think the wind has blown down some apples. We might as well eat them instead of leaving them for the slugs."

Merrylegs couldn't be resisted, so we broke off our long conversation and raised our spirits by munching some very sweet apples that lay scattered on the grass.

CHAPTER 11

Plain Speaking

The longer I lived at Birtwick Park, the prouder and happier I was to have such a place. Squire and Mrs. Gordon were respected and loved by everyone who knew them. They were good and kind to everyone, not only humans but also horses, donkeys, dogs, cats, cattle, and birds. They didn't abuse any creature. If Squire or Mrs. Gordon received word that any village child had abused any animal, they soon spoke to the child's parents about it.

For more than twenty years, Squire Gordon and Farmer Grey had tried to get a ban on checkreins on cart horses. Checkreins seldom were seen in our area. Sometimes, if Mrs. Gordon met a heavily loaded horse with their head strained up, she'd stop the carriage, get out, and tell the driver how foolish and cruel it was. I wish all ladies were like Mrs. Gordon.

Squire Gordon, too, protested whenever he

witnessed abuse. One morning, he was riding me home when we saw a powerful man driving toward us in a light, two-wheel carriage pulled by a beautiful little reddish-brown pony with slender legs and a sensitive face. When the pony came to the gates of Birtwick Park, he turned toward them. The man wrenched the pony's head around with such suddenness and force that he nearly threw the pony onto his haunches. The pony recovered himself and was going on when the man began to lash him furiously. The pony plunged forward, but the strong, heavy hand held him back with almost enough force to break his jaw, while the whip cut into him. It was a dreadful sight. I knew what terrible pain that treatment gave that delicate little mouth.

Squire Gordon gave me the word, and we were up alongside the carriage in a second. "Sawyer!" he cried. "Is that pony made of flesh and blood?"

"Flesh and blood and temper," Sawyer answered. He was a builder who often had been to Birtwick Park on business. "He's too fond of his own will. That doesn't suit me."

"Do you think that abuse will make him fond of *your* will?" Squire Gordon asked.

"He had no business making that turn. The road was straight ahead," Sawyer said roughly.

"You've often driven that pony to my place," Squire Gordon said. "His behavior only shows his memory and intelligence. How did he know that you weren't going there again? But that has little to do with it. It's never been my painful lot to witness crueler, more unmanly treatment of a pony. By behaving like this, you injure your own character as much as you injure your horse. Remember, God will judge us by our conduct—toward all creatures."

Squire Gordon rode me home slowly. I could tell by his voice that the incident had upset him.

Squire Gordon spoke just as freely to gentlemen of his own rank as to those below him. One day while we were out, we met Captain Langley, a friend of Squire Gordon. He was driving a four-wheel carriage pulled by a splendid pair of grays. After a little conversation, Captain Langley said, "What do you think of my new team, Mr. Gordon? You're the best judge of horses in these parts. I'd like your opinion."

Squire Gordon backed me up a little, to get a good view of them. "They're an uncommonly handsome pair. If their behavior is as good as their looks, you couldn't wish for better. But I see you still harass your horses and lessen their power."

"What do you mean? The checkreins? I know you object to them. The fact is, I like to see my horses hold their heads up."

"So do I, but I don't like to see their heads

held up. That takes all the shine out of it. You're a military man and no doubt like to see your regiment look good on parade. 'Heads up' and all that. You wouldn't take much credit for your drill if your men had their heads tied to a back-board! That might not do much harm on parade, except to harass and tire them, but how would it be in a bayonet charge against the enemy, when they need the free use of every muscle and all their strength thrown forward? I wouldn't give much for their chance of victory. It's the same with horses. You harass and dis-tress them and decrease their power. You won't let them throw their weight into their work. So they have to do too much with their joints and muscles, and it wears them down faster. Horses were meant to have their heads free. If we acted more in accordance with common sense instead of fashion, many things would work more easi-ly. You know as well as I do that if a horse makes a false step, they have much less chance of recovering themselves if their head and neck are fastened back. So won't you please remove the checkreins?"

"I'll think about it," Captain Langley replied. And he and Squire Gordon parted.

CHAPTER 12

A Stormy Day

One day in late autumn, Squire Gordon had a long journey to undertake on business. I was hitched to the two-seat cart, and John went with the squire. I always liked pulling the two-seat cart. It was light, and the high wheels ran along pleasantly. There had been a great deal of rain, and the wind was strong and blew fallen leaves across the road. We went along merrily until we came to the toll gate and low wooden bridge. The river banks were high, and the bridge went across level with them. Whenever the river was full, the water was nearly up to the bridge. However, people didn't mind this because substantial rails ran along the bridge's sides.

The man at the toll gate said that the river was rising fast. He feared it would be a bad night. Many of the meadows were under water. In one low part of the road, the water was halfway to my knees. The bottom was solid, though, and Squire Gordon drove gently.

When we got to the town, Squire Gordon's business engaged him a long time. We didn't start for home until late in the afternoon. The wind was much stronger then. Squire Gordon told John that he'd never been out in such a storm. I had the same thought as we went alongside woods where great branches were swaying like twigs.

"I wish we were out of this wooded area," Squire Gordon said.

"Yes, sir," John said. "It would be dangerous if one of those branches came down."

The words were scarcely out of John's mouth when there was a groan, crack, and splitting sound. Torn up by the roots, an oak came crashing down. It fell across the road right in front of us.

Frightened, I stopped and trembled, but I didn't turn around or run away. John jumped out and in a moment was at my head.

"That was a close call," Squire Gordon said. "What should we do?"

"Well, sir, we can't drive over that tree or get around it. All we can do is go back to the four crossways. It'll be a good six miles before we get back to the wooden bridge. We'll be late, but Black Beauty is fresh."

So we went back. By the time we got to the

bridge, it was nearly dark. We could just see that the water was over the bridge. Because that happened sometimes when there was flooding, Squire Gordon didn't stop. We were going along at a good pace, but the moment my feet touched the first part of the bridge, I knew something was wrong. I didn't dare go forward. I made a dead stop.

"Go on, Beauty," Squire Gordon said. He gave me a touch with the whip, but I didn't stir. He gave me a sharp cut. I jumped, but I didn't move forward.

"There's something wrong, sir," John said. He sprang out of the cart, came to my head, and looked all around. He tried to lead me forward. "What's the matter, Beauty?"

Just then the man at the toll gate on the other side of the bridge ran out of his house, waving a torch. "Stop! Stop!" he cried.

"What's wrong?" Squire Gordon shouted.

"The bridge is broken in the middle. Part of it has floated away. If you move forward, you'll be in the river."

"My God!" Squire Gordon exclaimed.

"Beauty!" John said with a tone of gratitude and admiration. He took my bridle and gently turned me around to the right-hand road by the riverside.

The sun had set. The wind had died down after the furious blast that tore up the tree. It grew darker and stiller. I trotted along quietly, the wheels hardly making a sound on the soft road.

For a good while neither Squire Gordon nor John spoke. Then Squire Gordon said in a solemn voice, "If Beauty had moved forward as I wanted him to, the bridge would have given way beneath us; we would have fallen into the river. The current was very strong. We probably would have drowned. God has given people reason, but an animal's understanding can be quicker and more perfect. I believe that Beauty has saved our lives."

John then told many stories of dogs and horses who had done wonderful things. "People don't value their animals half enough," he said, "or make friends of them as they should."

At last we came to Birtwick Park's gates and found the gardener watching for us. He said that Mrs. Gordon had been in a dreadful state ever since dark, fearing some accident, and that she'd sent James off on Justice toward the wooden bridge to inquire about us.

We saw a light at the hall door and the upper windows. As we came up, Mrs. Gordon ran out. "Are you really safe, my dear? I've been so anxious, imagining all sorts of things! You haven't had an accident?"

"No, my dear. But if Black Beauty hadn't been wiser than we were, we'd all have been carried down the river at the wooden bridge."

They went into the house, and John took me to the stable. He gave me an especially good supper that night: a good bran mash and some crushed beans with my oats. And he gave me an extra-thick bed of straw. I was glad because I was tired.

CHAPTER 13

The Devil's Trademark

One day when John and I had been out on some business of Squire Gordon's and were returning gently on a long, straight road, we saw a boy, at some distance, trying to get a pony to leap over a gate. The pony wouldn't take the leap, and the boy cut him with a whip. The pony turned off to one side, and the boy whipped him again. The pony then turned off to the other side. The boy got off and gave the pony a thrashing and punched him about the head. Then he got up again and tried to make the pony leap the gate, kicking him all the time. Still the pony refused.

When we were nearly to the spot, the pony put his head down, threw up his heels, and sent the boy off into a hedge. With the rein dangling from his head, the pony set off for home at a full gallop.

John said of the boy, "Serves him right."

"Ow! Ow!" the boy cried as he struggled among the thorns. "Come and help me out."

"No," John said. "You're where you belong. Maybe some scratches will teach you not to try to make ponies leap over gates that are too high for them. I know who you are: Bill Bushby. You should be ashamed."

John rode off. He said to himself, "That boy might be a liar as well as cruel. I'll go home by way of Farmer Bushby's and tell him what I saw."

We turned off to the right and soon came to Farmer Bushby's wood yard, within sight of his house. Farmer Bushby hurried out into the road. His wife was standing at the gate, looking frightened.

"Have you seen my boy?" Farmer Bushby asked as we came up. "He went out an hour ago on my black pony. The pony just came back without a rider."

"He *should* be without a rider," John said, "unless he can be ridden properly."

"What do you mean?" Farmer Bushby asked.

"I saw your son whipping, kicking, and punching that little pony because he wouldn't try to leap a gate that was too high for him. The pony behaved well and showed no vice. Finally, though, he threw up his heels and tipped your son into the thorn hedge. Your son wanted me to help him out, but I wouldn't. He hasn't broken any bones. He'll only get some scratches. I love horses, and it angers me to see them abused. It's a bad idea to aggravate horses until they use their heels."

Mrs. Bushby began to cry. "My poor Bill. I must go to him. He must be hurt."

"Go into the house, wife," Farmer Bushby said. "Bill needs to learn a lesson. This isn't the first or second time that he's abused that pony. I'm going to put a stop to this. I'm much obliged to you, Manly. Good evening."

So we went on.

John told James about the incident. James laughed and said, "Serves him right. I knew Bill Bushby at school. He put on lots of airs because he's a farmer's son. He swaggered around and bullied smaller boys. We older boys wouldn't put up with his nonsense. We let him know that we didn't consider farmers' sons any better than laborers'. One day, just before school's afternoon session, I found him at a large window catching flies and pulling off their wings. I gave him a box on the ear that laid him sprawling on the floor. He bellowed so much that the boys rushed in from the playground and the schoolmaster ran in from the road to see who was being murdered.

"I admitted what I'd done and said why. I

showed the schoolmaster the flies, some crushed and some crawling about helpless. I showed him the wings on the windowsill. The schoolmaster was angrier than I'd ever seen him. But because Bill was still howling and whining, like the coward that he is, the schoolmaster didn't punish him except to make him sit on a stool the rest of the afternoon and forbid him from going out to play the rest of that week. Then the schoolmaster talked to all of us boys about cruelty. He said how cruel and cowardly it is to hurt the weak and helpless. But what stuck in my mind was this: he said that cruelty is the devil's trademark and that whenever we see anyone who takes pleasure in cruelty, we should know that they belong to the devil, who is the great tormentor. On the other hand, whenever we see people who are kind to all creatures, we should know that they bear God's mark."

"Your schoolmaster never taught you a truer thing," John said. "There's no religion without love. People can talk as much as they like about their religion, but if it doesn't teach them to be good and kind to both people and animals, it's all a sham."

CHAPTER 14

James Howard

Early one December morning, Squire Gordon entered the stable while John was tending to me. The squire looked serious and held an open letter. John fastened the door of my stall, touched his cap as a sign of respect, and waited for orders.

"Good morning, John," Squire Gordon said. "I want to know if you have any complaint to make of James."

"Complaint, sir? No."

"Is he hardworking and respectful toward you?"

"Yes, sir. Always."

"He never slights his work when your back is turned?"

"Never, sir."

"Good. Do you have any reason to suspect, when he goes out with the horses to exercise them or to take a message, that he stops to visit friends, leaving the horses outside?"

"No, sir. Certainly not. If anyone has been saying that about James, I don't believe it. I don't know who's been trying to damage James's reputation, but I'll say this, sir: I've never had a steadier, smarter, more honest, or more pleasant young fellow in this stable. I trust his word and his work. He's gentle and clever with the horses. Whoever wants a character reference for James Howard can come to me," John said.

Squire Gordon smiled broadly.

James now entered with some oats.

"James, my lad, put the oats down and come here," the squire said. "I've received a letter from my brother-in-law, Sir Clifford Williams of Clifford Hall. He wants me to find him a trustworthy young groom about twenty years old, and I'm wondering if you would want the position. Sir Clifford's old coachman, who has lived with him thirty years, is getting feeble. Sir Clifford wants a young man to work with the coachman, learn his ways, and take his place when the old man retires. The young groom would have eighteen shillings a week at first, a stable suit, a driving suit, a bedroom over the coach house, and a boy to help him. Sir Clifford is a good master. I don't like the thought of parting with you. I know that John would lose his right hand if you left us. But if you got the position, it would be a good start for you."

"I certainly *would* lose my right hand," John said, "but I wouldn't stand in the way of James's advancement for anything."

"How old are you, James?" Squire Gordon asked.

"Nineteen next May, sir."

"That's young. What do you think, John?"

"Well, sir, it *is* young, but he's as steady as a man, strong, and well grown. Although he hasn't had much driving experience, he has a light, firm hand and a quick eye. He's very careful. I'm sure no horse of his will be ruined by not having his feet and shoes looked after."

"Your word will go the farthest, John," Squire Gordon said. "Sir Clifford adds in a postscript, 'If I could find a man trained by your John, I'd prefer him over any other.' So think it over, James. Talk to your mother at dinnertime, and let me know what you'd like to do."

A few days after this conversation, it was settled that James would go to Clifford Hall in a month or six weeks. Meanwhile, he would get all the driving practice that he could. I never knew the carriage to go out so often before. Previously when he'd gone on a quick errand, Squire Gordon had driven himself in the two-wheel carriage. Now when any member of the family went out for any reason, Ginger and I were hitched to the carriage and James drove us. At first, John rode with him on the driver's seat, telling him this and that. After that, James drove alone.

Ginger and I took Squire Gordon to all sorts of places in the city and down all sorts of streets. We were sure to go to the railway station just as a train was coming in and cabs, carriages, carts, and buses all were trying to get over the bridge at the same time. When the railway bell was ringing, that bridge required good horses and good drivers because it was narrow and there was a sharp turn up to the station where people easily could run into one another if they weren't careful.

CHAPTER 15

The Old Hostler

Squire and Mrs. Gordon decided to visit some friends who lived forty-six miles away. James was to drive them. The first day, we traveled thirty-two miles. There were some long, heavy hills, but James drove so carefully and thoughtfully that Ginger and I weren't at all harassed. He never forgot to put on the brake as we went downhill or take it off at the right place. He kept our feet on the smoothest part of the road. If the uphill was long, he set the carriage wheels a little across the road, so they wouldn't slip backward, and gave us a breather. These little things help horses very much, particularly if they also get kind words.

We stopped once or twice on the road. Just as the sun was setting, we reached the town where we were to spend the night. We stopped at the main hotel, in the marketplace. It was very large. We drove under an archway into a long yard. The stables and coach houses were at the yard's far end. Two hostlers came to take us to our stable.

The head hostler was a pleasant, active little man with a crooked leg and a striped yellow waistcoat. I never saw a man unbuckle a harness as quickly as he did. With a pat and a good word, he led me to a long stable with six stalls, with two horses in it. The other man brought Ginger. James stood by while we were rubbed down and cleaned.

I never was cleaned as lightly and quickly as by that little old man. When he finished, James stepped up and felt me over, as if he thought I couldn't be thoroughly done, but he found my coat as clean and smooth as silk.

"Well," James said, "I thought I was quick and our John even quicker, but you beat anyone I ever saw for being quick yet thorough."

"Practice makes perfect," the crooked little hostler said. "It would be a pity if I weren't perfect after forty years of practice. Once you get into the habit of being quick, it's just as easy as being slow—easier, in fact. It doesn't agree with my health to take twice as long as necessary to do a job. I've been around horses since I was twelve, including in hunting stables and racing stables. I was a jockey for several years. But at the Goodwood, the turf was slippery. My poor Larkspur fell, and I broke my knee, so I wasn't of any more use there. I couldn't live without horses, so I took to the hotels. It's a great pleasure to handle a horse like this: well bred, well-mannered, and well cared for. Bless you! I can tell how a horse has been treated. Let me handle a horse for twenty minutes, and I'll tell you what sort of groom they've had. Look at this one—pleasant, quiet, turns around just as you want him to, holds up his feet to be cleaned, and does anything else you want. Some horses are fidgety and nervous, won't move the right way, will start across the stall, toss up their head if you come near them, lay their ears back, and seem afraid. Some others will get ready to kick or bite. Poor things! I know what sort of treatment they've had. If a horse is timid, abuse makes them fearful. If they're high-spirited, it makes them vicious or dangerous. Their tempers are formed mostly when they're young. They're like children. Bring them up the right way, and when they're old, they're likely to behave the right way."

"I like to hear you talk," James said. "We hold the same views at our master's."

"Who's your master? From what I see, he must be a good one."

"Squire Gordon of Birtwick Park, on the other side of Beacon Hills."

"Ah! I've heard of him. Fine judge of horses, I've heard. Best rider in the county."

"I believe he is," James said, "but he rides very little now, since his son died."

"Ah! Poor gentleman. I read about that in the paper. A fine horse died, too, isn't that so?"

"Yes," James said. "He was a splendid creature, this one's brother and just like him."

"What a pity!" the old man said. "It was a bad place to leap, if I remember correctly: a thin fence at the top and a steep bank down to the stream. No chance for a horse to see where they're going. I like bold riding as much as anyone, but there are some leaps that only a very experienced huntsman should take. A man's life and a horse's life are worth more than catching a hare or fox. At least, they should be."

During this time the other man had finished tending to Ginger and had brought our corn. James and the old man left the stable together.

CHAPTER 16

The Fire

Later in the evening the second hostler brought in a traveler's horse. While he was cleaning the horse, a young man smoking a pipe strolled into the stable to gossip.

"Towler," the hostler said, "would you go up into the loft and put some hay into this horse's rack? Lay down your pipe first."

"All right," Towler said. He went up through the trapdoor, and I heard him step across the floor overhead and put down the hay.

James came in to look at Ginger and me before going to bed. Then the door was locked.

I don't know how long I slept, but I awoke feeling very uncomfortable. I got up. The air was thick and choking. I heard Ginger coughing, and one of the other horses seemed very restless. It was dark. I couldn't see anything, but the stable was full of smoke. I hardly could breathe.

The trapdoor had been left open, and I thought that the smoke came through it. I listened and heard a soft rushing noise and a low crackling and snapping. Something in the sound made me tremble all over. All of the other horses were awake. Some were pulling at their halters. Others were stamping.

At last I heard steps outside. The hostler who had put up the traveler's horse burst into the stable with a lantern and began to untie the horses and try to lead them out. He seemed so frightened and in such a hurry that I felt even more afraid. The first horse wouldn't go with him. He tried the second and third. They, too, wouldn't stir. He came to me next and tried to drag me out of the stall. That wasn't any use. He tried us all, then left the stable.

Of course we were wrong not to leave the stable, but we were immobilized by fear. Danger seemed to be all around, and we didn't trust a stranger. Everything was strange and uncertain.

The fresh air that had entered through the open door made it easier to breathe, but the rushing sound overhead grew louder. As I looked up through the bars of my empty hay rack, I saw a red light flickering on the wall. Then I heard a cry of "Fire!" outside.

The old hostler quietly and quickly entered. He got one horse out and went to another. The flames were playing around the trapdoor, and the roaring overhead was dreadful.

The next thing I heard was James's voice, quiet and cheerful as always. "Come, my beauties, it's time for us to be off. Wake up and come along." I stood nearest the door, so James came to me first. "Come, Beauty. On with your bridle, my boy. We'll soon be out of this smother." My bridle was on in no time. James removed his neck scarf and tied it lightly over my eyes. Patting and coaxing me, he led me out of the stable. When we were safe in the yard, he slipped the scarf off my eyes and shouted, "Here, somebody! Take this horse while I go back for the other."

A tall, broad man stepped forward and took me. James darted back into the stable. I set up a shrill whinny as I saw him go. Ginger told me afterward that my whinny probably saved her life, because if she hadn't heard me outside, she wouldn't have had the courage to come out.

There was much confusion in the yard. The horses were removed from the other stables, and the carriages and wagons were pulled out of the coach houses and sheds in case the flames spread further. On the other side of the yard, the windows had been thrown open, and people were shouting all sorts of things.

I kept my eyes on the stable door, where the smoke poured out thicker than ever and I could see flashes of red light.

Presently I heard Squire Gordon's voice, loud and clear, above all the stir and din. "James Howard! James Howard! Are you there?"

There was no answer. I heard a crash of something falling inside the stable. The next moment I gave a loud, joyful neigh because I saw James coming through the smoke leading Ginger. She was coughing violently.

"My brave lad!" Squire Gordon said, laying his hand on James's shoulder. "Are you hurt?"

James shook his head because he couldn't speak yet.

The big man who held me said, "Yes, he's a brave lad. No doubt about it."

"When you have your breath, James, we'll get out of here as quickly as we can," Squire Gordon said.

We were moving toward the entry when the sound of galloping feet and loud rumbling wheels came from the marketplace.

"It's the fire engine! The fire engine!" two or three people shouted. "Stand back! Make way!"

Clattering and thundering over the stones, two horses dashed into the yard with a heavy engine behind them. The firemen leaped to the ground. There was no need to ask where the fire was. It was rolling up in a great blaze from the roof.

We got out as fast as we could into the broad, quiet marketplace. The stars were shining. Except for the noise behind us, everything was still.

Squire Gordon led the way to a large hotel on the other side. As soon as the hostler came, Squire Gordon said, "James, I must hurry to your mistress. I entrust the horses to you. Order whatever you think is needed." With that, he quickly walked away.

There was a dreadful sound before we got into our stalls—the shrieks of the poor horses who were left burning to death in the stable. It was terrible and made Ginger and me very sad. We were taken in and well cared for.

The next morning Squire Gordon came to see how we were and to speak to James. I didn't hear much because the hostler was rubbing me down, but I could see that James looked very happy. Squire Gordon seemed proud of him.

Mrs. Gordon had been so upset by the fire that our journey was delayed until the afternoon. James went to the inn to see about our harness and the carriage and to hear more about the fire. When he returned, we heard him tell the hostler about it. At first no one could guess the fire's cause, but finally a man said that he'd seen Dick Towler go into the stable smoking a pipe and come out without a pipe. Then the under-hostler said that he had asked Towler to go up into the loft to put down some hay but had told him to lay down his pipe first. Towler denied taking the pipe with him, but no one believed him. I remembered John Manly's rule never to allow a pipe in the stable and thought it should be the rule everywhere. James said that the stable's roof had fallen in and that only the black walls still were standing. The two poor horses who couldn't be rescued were buried under the burned rafters.

CHAPTER 17

James's Departure

The rest of our journey was easy. A little after sunset we reached the house of Squire Gordon's friend. We were taken into a clean, snug stable.

A kind coachman made us very comfortable. He seemed to admire James when he heard about the fire. "One thing is clear, young man," he said. "Your horses trust you. It's one of the hardest things in the world to get horses out of a stable when there's a fire or flood. I don't know why they won't come out, but they won't—not one in twenty."

We stayed at this place three days and then returned home. We were glad to be in our own stable again, and John was equally glad to see us.

Before John and James left us for the night, James said, "Who will be taking my place?"

"Little Joe Green," John said.

"Joe Green! He's a child!"

"He's fourteen and a half," John said.

"But he's such a little guy!"

"Yes, he's small, but he's quick, willing, and kind. He wants to come, and his father would like it. The master would like to give him the chance. He said if I thought that Joe wouldn't do, he'd look for a bigger boy, but I said I was quite willing to try Joe for six weeks."

"Six weeks!" James said. "It'll be six months before he can be of much use! It will make a lot of work for you, John."

"Well," John said with a laugh, "work and I are good friends. I've never been afraid of work."

"You're a good man. I hope I'll be like you."

"I was the same age as Joe when my parents died of scarlet fever within ten days of each other. My crippled sister Nelly and I were left alone in the world, without any relative we could look to for help. I was a farmer's boy, not earning enough to support myself, much less the two of us. Nelly would have gone to the workhouse if Mrs. Gordon hadn't come to our aid. Nelly calls her "my angel" and with good reason. Mrs. Gordon rented a room for Nelly with old Widow Mallet. She also gave Nelly knitting and needlework. When Nelly was ill, Mrs. Gordon sent her dinners and other things to help her along. She was like a mother to her. Squire Gordon took me into the stable under old Norman, who was the coachman then. I was given food at the house, a bed in the loft, a suit of clothes, and three shillings a week, so I was able to help Nelly. Norman was kind, too. He could have said that at his age he couldn't be bothered with a raw farm boy like me. Instead he was like a father to me. He took no end of pains with me. When Norman died some years later, I took his place. Now I have top wages and savings, and Nelly is happy. So you see, James, I'm not someone who should turn up his nose at a little boy and vex a good, kind master. I'll miss you very much, but we'll pull through. There's nothing like doing a kindness when you have the chance. I'm glad I can do it."

"Then, you don't agree with the saying, 'Everybody should look after themselves and take care of Number One.'"

"No, indeed," John said. "Where would Nelly and I be if master, mistress, and Norman had taken care of no one but Number One? Nelly would be in the workhouse, and I'd be hoeing turnips. Where would Black Beauty and Ginger be if you'd thought only of Number One? Burned to death! No, Jim. That's a selfish, heathenish saying. Anyone who thinks they should only take care of Number One isn't fit to live."

James laughed, but his voice was thick with emotion when he said, "Except for my mother, you've been my best friend. I hope you won't forget me."

"Of course I won't!" John said. "If I ever can do anything for you, please let me know."

The next day, Joe came to the stables to learn everything that he could before James left. He learned to sweep the stable and bring in the straw and hay. He helped clean the harness and wash the carriage. Because Joe was too short to groom Ginger and me, James had him groom Merrylegs, who would be under his care. Joe was a nice, bright little fellow. He always came to his work whistling.

Merrylegs was annoyed at being "mauled," as he put it, "by a boy who knows nothing." However, toward the end of the second week Merrylegs told me that he thought Joe would turn out well.

At last the day came when James had to leave us. He looked very downhearted. "I'm leaving a lot behind," he told John. "My mother, you, a good master and mistress, and the horses, especially my Merrylegs. I won't know anyone at the new place. If it weren't that I'll have a higher position and be able to help my mother better, I don't think I would have agreed to leave. This is hard, John."

"Yes, my lad. When you leave home for the first time, you're bound to feel it keenly. Cheer up. You'll make friends. I'm sure you'll do well, and that will be a fine thing for your mother. She'll be proud that you've gotten such a good position."

Everyone was sorry to lose James. For several days Merrylegs grieved so much that he hardly ate. Then John took Merrylegs out with a leading rein and had him trot and gallop by my side during some of my morning exercise sessions. This raised the little fellow's spirits, and he soon was cheerful again.

Thomas Green, Joe's father, often came in and gave some help because he understood the work. Joe took great pains to learn, and John was pleased with him.

CHAPTER 18

Going for the Doctor

One night a few days after James had left, I had eaten my hay and was lying down in my straw asleep when I was suddenly roused by the stable bell ringing loudly. I heard the door of John's house open and heard him run to the hall. He was back again in no time. He unlocked the stable door and came in, calling, "Wake up, Beauty! You must go quickly now." Almost before I could think, John placed the saddle on my back and the bridle on my head.

John took me up to the hall door at a quick trot. Squire Gordon stood there with a lamp in his hand. He said, "Ride for your life, John—that is, for your mistress's life. There isn't a moment to lose. Give this note to Dr. White. Rest Beauty at the inn, and be back as soon as you can."

John said, "Yes, sir," and was on my back in a minute.

The gardener who lived at the lodge had

heard the bell ring and already had opened the gate. Away we went through the park, through the village, and down the hill until we came to the toll gate.

John called loudly and pounded on the door of the gatekeeper's house. The gatekeeper came out and flung open the gate. "Keep the gate open for the doctor," John said. "Here's the money." And off we went again.

Before us was a long, level road by the riverside. John said, "Do your best, Beauty." For two miles I galloped as fast as I could. I didn't need any whip or spur. I don't believe that my grandfather, who won the race at Newmarket, could have gone faster.

When we came to the bridge, John pulled me up a little and patted my neck. "Well done, Beauty! Good fellow." He would have let me go slower, but my spirit was up.

I was off again as fast as before. The air was frosty and the moon bright. It was very pleasant. We came through a village, then a dark wood. We went uphill, then downhill. After eight miles' run, we came to the town. We went through the streets and into the marketplace. It was quiet except for the clatter of my feet on the stones. Everyone was asleep. The church clock struck three as we drew up to Dr. White's door.

John rang the bell twice and then pounded at the door.

A window was thrown open. Dr. White, in his nightcap, put his head out and asked, "What is it?"

"Mrs. Gordon is very ill, sir. Master wants you to go at once. He thinks she'll die if you can't get there. Here's a note."

"I'll come," Dr. White said. He shut the window and soon was at the door. "The problem is, my horse has been out all day and is quite tired. Someone just sent for my son, who took the other horse. May I have your horse?"

"He has galloped nearly the whole way. I was supposed to give him a rest here. But I think that Squire Gordon would consent if you think fit, sir."

"All right," he said. "I'll soon be ready."

John stood by me and stroked my neck. I was very hot. The doctor came out with his riding whip. "You don't need that, sir," John said. "Black Beauty will go until he drops. Take good care of him. I don't want any harm to come to him."

"Of course, John," the doctor said.

In a minute Dr. White and I had left John far behind. The doctor was heavier than John and not as good a rider, but I did my best. The man at the toll gate had it open. When we came to the hill, the doctor drew me up. "Now, my good fellow," he said, "take a breather." I was glad we paused because I was nearly exhausted.

The breather helped me to go on.

Soon we were in Birtwick Park. Joe was at the lodge gate. Squire Gordon was at the hall door because he'd heard us coming. He didn't say a word. Dr. White went into the house with him, and Joe led me to the stable.

I was glad to be home. My legs shook. I could only stand and pant. I didn't have a dry hair on my body. Sweat ran down my legs, and I steamed all over. Joe was young and knew very little. He rubbed my legs and chest, but he didn't put a warm cloth on me. He must have thought that I wouldn't like that because I was so hot. He gave me a bucketful of water to drink. It was cold and good. I drank it all. Then he gave me some hay and corn, and, no doubt thinking that he'd done the right things, went away.

Soon I started to shake and turned deadly cold. My legs, loins, and chest ached. I felt sore all over. I wanted my warm, thick cloth. I stood and trembled. I wanted John, but he had eight miles to walk, so I lay down in my straw and tried to sleep.

After a long time I heard John at the door. I gave a low moan because I was in great pain. He was at my side in a moment, stooping down by me. I couldn't tell him how I felt, but he seemed to know. He covered me with two or three warm cloths and then ran to the house for some hot water. He made me some warm gruel, which I drank.

John was very upset. He said to himself, "Stupid boy! Stupid boy! No cloth put on. I bet the water was cold, too."

I was very ill. My lungs were greatly inflamed. I couldn't breathe without pain. John nursed me night and day. He got up two or three times during the night to come to me.

Squire Gordon, too, often came to see me. "My poor Beauty," he said one day. "My good horse, you saved your mistress's life. Yes, Beauty, you saved her life."

I was very glad to hear that. The doctor, I heard, had said that if he and I had been just a little longer in coming, it would have been too late.

John told Squire Gordon that he never saw a horse go so fast. "It was as if Beauty knew what was wrong," John said.

Of course I knew. At least, I knew this: John and I must go as fast as possible, for the mistress's sake.

CHAPTER 19

Only Ignorance

I don't know how long I was ill. The horse doctor came every day. I felt so weak that I thought I was dying. I think everyone else thought so, too.

Ginger and Merrylegs had been moved into the other stable so I'd stay quiet. Fever made my hearing more sensitive. Any little sound seemed loud. I could distinguish everyone's footsteps going to and from the house.

One night John had to give me medicine. Mr. Green came in to help him. After I'd taken the medicine and John had made me as comfortable as he could, he said he'd stay half an hour to see how the medicine settled. Mr. Green said he'd stay too. The two of them went and sat on a bench that had been brought into Merrylegs' stall. They put the lantern at their feet so the light wouldn't disturb me.

For a while both men sat silent. Then Mr. Green said in a low voice, "John, I wish you'd say something kind to Joe. He's brokenhearted. He barely eats and never smiles. He says he knows it was all his fault, although he did his best. He says that if Beauty dies, no one ever will speak to him again. It breaks my heart to hear him. Please give him a kind word. He isn't a bad boy."

After a short pause, John said, "I know that Joe didn't mean any harm, Tom. I never said that he did. I know he isn't a bad boy. But I'm hurting too. That horse is the pride of my heart, to say nothing of his being a favorite of the master and mistress. To think that his life might be flung away in this way is more than I can bear. But if you think I'm being hard on the boy, I'll try to give him a good word tomorrow, if Beauty is better."

"Thank you, John. I knew you didn't mean to be hard. I'm glad you see it was only ignorance."

John's voice almost startled me as he answered passionately, "Only ignorance! Next to wickedness, ignorance is the worst thing in the world. Heaven only knows which of the two does more harm."

I heard no more of the conversation. The medicine put me to sleep. In the morning I felt much better.

CHAPTER 20

Joe Green

Joe Green made good progress. He learned quickly and was so attentive and careful that John began to trust him in many things. However, because he was small, he seldom was allowed to exercise Ginger or me.

One morning John was out with Justice in the luggage cart when Squire Gordon needed a note to be taken immediately to a gentleman's house about three miles away. Squire Gordon sent orders for Joe to saddle me and bring the note, adding the warning that he should ride carefully.

The note was delivered, and Joe and I were quietly returning when we came to the brick field. We saw a cart heavily loaded with bricks. The wheels were stuck in the stiff mud of some deep ruts. The carter was shouting and mercilessly flogging the two horses hitched to the cart. The horses were straining and struggling with all their might to drag the cart out, but they could-n't move it. Sweat streamed from their legs and flanks; their sides heaved; every muscle strained. Yet the man, fiercely pulling at the head of the front horse, lashed them brutally.

Joe pulled up. "Stop!" he said. "Don't flog horses like that. The wheels are stuck. They can't move the cart."

The man took no heed but went on lashing.

"Stop I say!" Joe said. "I'll help you lighten the cart. They can't move it as it is."

"Mind your own business, you impudent young rascal!" The man, who clearly had been drinking, was in a towering rage. He reapplied the whip.

Joe turned my head, and the next moment we were galloping toward the house of the master brickmaker. I don't know if John would have approved of our pace, but Joe and I were of one mind and so angry that we couldn't have gone slower.

The house stood by the road. Joe knocked at the door and shouted, "Hello! Is Mr. Clay home?"

Mr. Clay came out. "Hello, young man! You seem in a hurry. Any orders from the squire this morning?"

"No, Mr. Clay, but there's a fellow in your brickyard flogging two horses to death. I told him to stop, and he wouldn't. I said I'd help him lighten the cart, and he wouldn't let me, so I've come to tell you. Please go, sir." Joe's voice shook with agitation.

"Thank you, lad," Mr. Clay said. He started to run for his hat, then paused. "Will you testify to what you saw if I bring the man up before a magistrate?"

"Yes," Joe said, "gladly."

Mr. Clay set off, and we headed home at a smart trot.

"What's the matter, Joe? You look angry all over," John said as the boy flung himself from the saddle.

"I *am* angry all over." In hurried, excited words Joe told everything that had happened.

"You did the right thing, Joe, whether the man gets a summons or not. Many people would have ridden by and told themselves it wasn't their business to interfere. In my view, whenever anyone sees cruelty, it *is* their business to interfere. You did the right thing."

Joe calmed down. He was glad that John approved of him. He cleaned my feet and rubbed me down with a more confident hand than usual.

John and Joe were just going home to dinner when the footman came to the stable to say that Joe was wanted immediately in Squire Gordon's study. A man had been charged with abusing horses, and Joe's testimony was wanted.

The boy flushed up to his forehead, but his eyes sparkled. "And they'll have it," he said. Joe straightened his necktie and jacket and was off in a moment.

Because Squire Gordon was a county magistrate, cases often were brought to him to settle.

The next time Joe entered the stable, he was in high spirits. He gave me an affectionate pat and said, "We won't stand by and see such things done, will we, Beauty?"

We heard afterward that Joe's testimony had been so firm, and the horses had been found in such an exhausted and abused state, that the carter was called to stand trial and could be sentenced to two or three months in prison.

A wonderful change came over Joe. John said that Joe grew an inch taller that week, and I believe he did. He was as kind and gentle as before, but there was more determination in everything that he did. He had jumped from boy to man.

CHAPTER 21

The Parting

I had lived in Birtwick Park three years when sad changes began. Mrs. Gordon was ill. The doctor was often at the house, and Squire Gordon looked grave and anxious. Then we heard that Mrs. Gordon had been advised to leave England and go to a warm country for two or three years. The news fell on the household like the tolling of a death bell. Everyone was sorry. Squire Gordon began to arrange to break up his establishment and leave England. We horses talked about this constantly.

John went about his work sadly and silently. Joe scarcely whistled anymore. There was a great deal of coming and going. Ginger and I had full work.

The first to leave were Jessie and Flora, with their governess. They came to bid us goodbye. They hugged poor Merrylegs like an old friend, and so he was.

Then we heard what had been arranged for us. Squire Gordon had sold Ginger and me to his friend Lord Gerald, the Earl of Westford, because he thought we'd be well cared for.

He'd sold Merrylegs to the vicar, Mr. Blomefield, who wanted a pony for his wife. The sale was on condition that Merrylegs never be sold again. Joe was hired to take care of Merrylegs and help in the vicar's house, so I thought that Merrylegs was well-off.

John was offered several good positions, but he turned them all down. He said he'd wait a while and look around.

The evening before the family left, Squire Gordon came into the stable to give some directions and pat his horses for the last time. He was very sad. I knew that from his voice. I believe we horses can tell more from people's voices than many people can.

"Have you decided what you're going to do, John?" Squire Gordon asked. "You haven't accepted any job offers."

"I've decided that a position with some first-rate colt breaker and horse trainer would be the right thing for me. Abuse frightens and ruins many horses. That shouldn't be. I always get on well with horses. If I can help some of them get a good start, I'll feel that I'm doing something worthwhile. What do you think, sir?"

"I can't think of anyone better suited to

such a job," Squire Gordon said. "You understand horses, and they understand you. In time you might set up your own business. If I can help you in any way, write to me. I'll speak to my agent in London and leave a letter of reference with him." Squire Gordon gave John the name and address. Then he thanked him for his long, faithful service.

That was too much for John. "Please don't, sir. I can't bear it. You and my dear mistress have done so much for me that I never can repay you. I won't ever forget you, sir. I hope to God that some day mistress will be fully well."

Squire Gordon gave John his hand but didn't speak. They left the stable.

The sad last day arrived. The footman had gone the day before with the heavy luggage. Now there were only Squire Gordon, Mrs. Gordon, and her maid.

Ginger and I brought the carriage up to the hall door for the last time. The servants brought out cushions and rugs and many other things. When everything was arranged, Squire Gordon came down the steps carrying his wife in his arms. He placed her carefully in the carriage while the house servants stood around crying.

"Goodbye again," Squire Gordon said. "We won't forget any of you." He got in. "Drive on, John."

Joe jumped up, and we trotted slowly

through the park and village, where people were standing at their doors to have a last look and say, "God bless you."

When we reached the railway station, Mrs. Gordon walked from the carriage to the waiting room. I heard her say, "Goodbye, John. God bless you."

John didn't answer. I think he couldn't speak. As soon as Joe had taken the things out of the carriage, John called him to stand by the horses while he went onto the platform. Poor Joe! He stood alongside our heads to hide his tears.

Soon the train came puffing into the station. Several minutes later the doors were shut, the guard whistled, and the train glided away, leaving behind white smoke and heavy hearts.

When it was out of sight, John came back. He took the reins, mounted the driver's seat, and with Joe drove slowly home. But it wasn't our home anymore.

CHAPTER 22

Earlshall

The next morning after breakfast, Joe hitched Merrylegs to Mrs. Gordon's low two-wheel carriage, to take him to the vicarage. Joe came and said goodbye to us, and Merrylegs neighed to us from the yard.

John put the saddle on Ginger and the leading rein on me, and we went about fifteen miles to Earlshall Park, where Lord Gerald lived. The house was very fine, and there were many stables. We went into the stable yard through a stone gateway, and John asked for Mr. York, our new coachman.

It was some time before York came. He was a fine-looking middle-aged man. His voice conveyed that he expected to be obeyed. He was friendly and polite to John. After glancing at us, he called a groom to take us to our stalls and invited John to take some refreshment.

Ginger and I were taken to a light, airy stable and placed in adjoining stalls, where we were rubbed down and fed. In about half an hour, John and York came in to see us.

After carefully looking at us both, York said, "Mr. Manly, I see no fault in these horses, but we all know that horses, like people, have their peculiarities and sometimes need particular treatment. Is there anything about either of these horses that you'd like to mention?"

"I don't think there's a better pair of horses in all of England," John said. "I'm sorely grieved to part with them. The black one has the sweetest nature I've ever known. I think he's never known a harsh word or a blow since he was born. He seems to take great pleasure in doing whatever a person wishes. In contrast, the chestnut mare was abused. The dealer told us that. When she came to us, she was snappish and suspicious. But when she realized that she was safe with us, she became sweet and obliging. For three years now, she hasn't shone the least sign of temper. If she's treated well, there isn't a better, more willing horse. But she's naturally more high-strung than the black horse. Flies irritate her more. Anything wrong with her harness bothers her more. If she were abused, she'd likely strike back. You know that many high-spirited horses will."

"Of course," York said. "I fully understand,

but it isn't easy in stables as large as these to have all the grooms be just what they should be. I do my best, and I have to leave it at that. I'll remember what you've said about the mare."

They were leaving the stable when John stopped and said, "I should mention that we've never used a checkrein with either of them. The black horse never has had one on, and the dealer said that a checkrein spoiled the other's temper."

"Well," York said, "they'll have to wear a checkrein here. I prefer a loose rein myself, and Lord Gerald always is reasonable about horses, but Lady Helen—that's another thing. She insists on style. She demands that her carriage horses be reined up tightly. I avoid using a checkrein whenever possible, but the rein must be tight up when Lady Helen rides."

"I'm sorry to hear that, really sorry," John said. "I must go now, or I'll miss my train." He came to Ginger and me to pat and speak to us for the last time. His voice was very sad.

I held my face close to him. That was all I could do to say goodbye.

Then he was gone. I haven't seen him since.

The next day, Lord Gerald came to look at us. He seemed pleased with our appearance. "I have great confidence in these horses. My friend Mr. Gordon has highly recommended them," he said. "They don't match in color, but they'll do very well for the carriage while we're in the country. Before we go to London, I must try to match Baron. The black horse, I believe, is perfect for riding."

York then told him what John had said about us.

"Well," Lord Gerald said, "you must keep an eye on the mare and leave the checkrein somewhat loose at first. I'll mention this to Lady Helen."

In the afternoon we were harnessed and hitched to the carriage. As the stable clock struck three, we were led around to the front of the house. It was very grand, three or four times as large as the house at Birtwick but not half as pleasant. Two footmen stood ready, dressed in uniforms, with scarlet breeches and white stockings.

Presently we heard the rustling of silk as Lady Helen came down the flight of stone steps. She stepped around to look at us. She was a tall, proud-looking woman. She seemed displeased about something, but she didn't say anything. She got into the carriage. This was the first time I'd worn a checkrein. Although it was a nuisance not to be able to let my head down now and then, it didn't pull my head any higher than I was accustomed to holding it. I felt anxious about Ginger, but she seemed quiet and content.

The next day at three, we were at the door again. The footmen were as before. We heard the silk dress rustle, and Lady Helen came down the steps. In an imperious voice she said, "York, you must put those horses' heads higher. They aren't fit to be seen."

York got down and respectfully said, "I beg your pardon, my lady, but these horses aren't accustomed to being reined up. My lord said it would be safer to get them used to it by degrees. But if your ladyship wishes it, I can tighten the reins a little."

"Do so," she said.

York came around to our heads and shortened the reins by one hole. Every little bit makes a difference, and that day we had a steep hill to climb. I began to understand what I'd heard about checkreins. I wanted to put my head forward and take the carriage up with a will, as I was accustomed to. Instead I had to pull with my head up. That took all the spirit out of me and strained my back and legs.

When we came in, Ginger said, "Now you see what it's like, and this isn't nearly as bad as it can get. If it doesn't get much worse than this, I won't protest, because otherwise we're treated well here. But if they rein me up tight, let them look out! I can't bear it, and I won't."

Day by day, hole by hole, our checkreins were shortened. Instead of looking forward with pleasure to having my harness put on, as I used to, I began to dread it. Ginger, too, seemed restless, although she said very little. At last I thought the worst was over. For several days there was no more shortening. I determined to make the best of it and do my duty, although it was now a constant harassment.

CHAPTER 23

A Strike for Liberty

One day Lady Helen came down later than usual. Her silk rustled more than ever. "Drive to the Duchess of Blenning," she said and then after a pause, "Aren't you ever going to get those horses' heads up, York? Raise them at once. Let's not have any more of this nonsense."

York came to me first, while the groom stood at Ginger's head. He drew my head back and fixed the rein so tight that it was almost unbearable.

Then York went to Ginger, who was impatiently jerking her head up and down against the bit, as was her way now. She knew what was coming. The moment York took the rein off the harness ring to shorten it, she reared up so suddenly that he was hit roughly in the nose and his hat was knocked off. The groom nearly was thrown off his legs. They both flew to Ginger's head, but she was a match for them. She plunged, reared, and kicked. Finally she kicked the carriage pole and fell down after accidentally giving me a severe blow on my near quarter. York promptly sat on her head to prevent her from struggling. He called out, "Unbuckle the black horse! Run for the winch and unscrew the carriage pole! Cut the trace here, somebody, if you can't unhitch it!"

One of the footmen ran for the winch. Another brought a knife from the house. The groom set me free from Ginger and the carriage and led me to my stall. He turned me in as I was and ran back to York.

I was very agitated about what had happened. I wanted to kick or rear. I stood, angry, with a sore leg, my head still strained up to the harness ring on the saddle. I had no power to get it down. I was miserable and wanted to kick the first person who came near me.

Before long, two grooms led Ginger in. She was badly bruised.

York came with her and gave his orders. Then he came to look at me. In a moment he let down my head. "Confound these checkreins!" he said to himself. "I knew we'd soon have trouble. Lord Gerald will be very annoyed. But if he can't get his wife to be reasonable, *I* certainly can't. If she doesn't get to the duchess's garden party, it's too bad about her."

York felt me all over and soon found the place above my ankle where I'd been kicked. It was swollen and painful. He ordered it to be sponged with hot water. Then lotion was applied.

Lord Gerald was upset when he learned what had happened. He blamed York for giving in to Lady Helen. York replied that from now on he'd prefer to receive his orders only from Lord Gerald.

Ginger never was hitched to the carriage again. When she had completely healed, one of Lord Gerald's younger sons said he'd like to have her. He was sure she'd make a good hunter.

I still was forced to pull the carriage. I had a new partner, Max, who was used to the tight rein. I asked him, "How do you bear it?"

"I bear it because I have to," he said. "But it's shortening my life, and it will shorten yours if you have to stick to it."

"Do you think that people know how bad it is for us?"

"The dealers and horse doctors certainly know," he said. "Once, a dealer was training another horse and me to go as a pair. He was getting our heads up a little higher each day. A gentleman asked him why he did that. He answered, 'People won't buy them unless we do. London people want their horses to carry their heads high and step high. It's very bad for the horses, but it's good for business. The horses soon wear out, and people buy another pair.'"

It would be hard to describe what I suffered with that checkrein for four long months. If the situation had continued much longer, either my health or my temper would have given way. Previously I'd never known what it is to foam at the mouth. Now the action of the sharp bit on my tongue and jaw, and the constrained position of my head and throat, always caused me to foam. Some people like to see that and say, "What fine-spirited horses!" But it's just as unnatural for horses to foam at the mouth as it is for humans. It's a sure sign of discomfort. In addition, there was pressure on my windpipe, which often made breathing very uncomfortable. When I returned from my work, my neck and chest were strained and painful, my mouth and tongue were tender, and I felt worn and depressed.

In my old home I'd always known that John and Squire Gordon were my friends. Here, although I was treated well in many ways, I had no human friend. I'm sure that York knew how much the rein hurt me, but he did nothing to stop it.

CHAPTER 24

A Runaway Horse

Early in the spring Lord Gerald and some members of his family went up to London and took York with them. Lady Anne was among the family members who remained at Earlshall.

Lady Anne was a merry, gentle person who liked to go horseback riding. She chose me for her horse and named me Black Auster. I enjoyed my rides with Lady Anne in the clear, cold air. Sometimes we were accompanied by another rider and horse, either Ginger or Lizzie. Lizzie was a reddish-brown mare, almost thorough-bred, a great favorite with the gentlemen because of her fine action and lively spirit. But Ginger, who knew her better than I did, told me that Lizzie was nervous.

Lady Anne's cousin Colonel Blantyre was staying at the hall. He repeatedly rode Lizzie and praised her. One day Lady Anne ordered the ladies' side-saddle to be put on Lizzie and the men's saddle to be put on me.

When we came to the door, Colonel Blantyre seemed very uneasy. "What's this?" he asked. "Are you tired of your good Black Auster?"

"Not at all," Lady Anne replied, "but I'll let you ride him for once. I'll try your charming Lizzie. You must confess that in size and appearance she's far more like a lady's horse than my own favorite."

"I advise you not to ride her," Colonel Blantyre said. "She's a charming creature but too nervous for a lady. I assure you, she isn't perfectly safe. I beg you to have the saddles changed."

"My dear cousin," Lady Anne said, laughing, "don't trouble yourself about me. I've been riding since I was a baby. I've followed the hounds many times, although I know you don't approve of ladies hunting. I intend to try Lizzie, whom you gentlemen are so fond of. So please help me mount."

Colonel Blantyre placed Lady Anne on the saddle, looked to the bit and curb, gently put the reins in her hand, and then mounted me.

As we were moving off, a footman came out with a slip of paper and message from Lady Harriet, another member of the family who had remained at Earlshall. "Will you convey this question to Dr. Ashley and bring the answer?" the footman asked Colonel Blantyre.

The village was about a mile away, and Dr. Ashley's house was the last in it. We went along gaily until we came to the doctor's gate. There was a short drive up to the house between tall evergreens. Colonel Blantyre alighted at the gate and was going to open it for Lady Anne, but she said, "I'll wait for you here. You can hang Auster's rein on the gate."

Colonel Blantyre looked at her doubtfully. "I won't be more than five minutes," he said.

"No hurry. Lizzie and I won't run away."

Colonel Blantyre hung my rein on one of the iron spikes and soon was hidden among the trees.

Lizzie was standing quietly by the side of the road a few paces off, with her back to me. Lady Anne was sitting easily with a loose rein, humming a song. I listened to Colonel Blantyre's footsteps until they reached the house. I heard him knock at the door.

Across the road was a meadow, whose gate stood open. Some cart horses and several young colts came trotting out in a disorderly way while a boy behind them cracked a large whip. The colts were wild and frolicsome. One of them bolted across the road and blundered up against Lizzie's hind legs.

Lizzie gave a violent kick and dashed off in a headlong gallop. It was so sudden that Lady Anne nearly was unseated.

I gave a loud, shrill neigh for help. I neighed again and again, pawing the ground and tossing my head to get the rein loose. I didn't have to wait long. Colonel Blantyre came running to the gate. He looked around anxiously and caught sight of Lady Anne, already far down the road. In an instant he sprang into the saddle. I needed no whip or spur; I was as anxious as my rider. Colonel Blantyre saw this and gave me a free rein. He leaned a little forward, and we dashed after Lizzie and Lady Anne.

The road was straight for about a mile and a half. Then it bent to the right, after which it divided into two roads. Long before we came to the bend, Lady Anne was out of sight. Which way had she turned?

A woman was standing at her garden gate, shading her eyes with her hand and looking anxiously up the road.

Scarcely drawing the rein, Colonel Blantyre shouted, "Which way did she go?"

"To the right!" the woman cried, pointing.

Away we went up the right-hand road. For a moment we caught sight of Lady Anne. Then another bend hid her again. Several times we caught glimpses. We scarcely seemed to gain on Lizzie.

An old road-mender was standing near a heap of stones, his shovel dropped and his hands raised. As we neared, he gestured that he wanted to speak. Colonel Blantyre drew the rein a little. "She turned off to the common, sir," the road-mender said. "To the common."

I knew this common very well. It was mostly uneven ground covered with heather and furze bushes, with a scrubby thorn tree here and there. There also were open spaces of short grass, with anthills and molehills everywhere. It was the worst place I knew for a headlong gallop.

We hardly had turned onto the common when we again caught sight of Lady Anne's green riding outfit, flying on before us. Lady Anne's hat was gone. Her long brown hair streamed behind her. Her head and body were thrown back, as if she was pulling with all her strength but was nearly exhausted. The ground's roughness had considerably reduced Lizzie's speed. It seemed that we might overtake her.

While we'd been on the high road, Colonel Blantyre had given me free rein. Now, with a light hand and practiced eye, he guided me over the ground in such a masterly way that my pace scarcely slackened. We gained on Lizzie.

About halfway across the heath was a wide, recently cut dike. The earth from the cutting was cast up roughly on the other side. I thought, "Surely that will stop them." But no. With scarcely a pause, Lizzie took the leap, stumbled among the rough clods, and fell. She got back up, riderless.

Colonel Blantyre groaned. "Auster, do your best!" He gave me a steady rein. I gathered myself together and, with one determined leap, cleared both the dike and the bank.

Lady Anne lay motionless in the heather, with her face to the earth. Colonel Blantyre kneeled and called her name. No response. He gently turned her face upward. Her face was ghastly white. Her eyes were closed.

"Annie, dear Annie, please speak!" Still no answer. Colonel Blantyre unbuttoned Lady Anne's jacket, loosened her collar, felt her hands and wrist, then started up and looked around frantically for help.

Nearby two men were cutting turf. Colonel Blantyre's "Hello!" brought them to the spot.

The foremost man seemed much troubled at the sight of Lady Anne and asked what he could do.

"Can you ride?"

"I'm not much of a horseman, sir, but I'd risk my neck for Lady Anne. She was uncommon good to my wife this winter."

"Then mount this horse, my friend. You'll be safe. Ride to Dr. Ashley, and ask him to come at once. Then go on to Earlshall, tell them all that you know, and ask them to send me the carriage, with help and Lady Anne's maid. I'll stay here."

"I'll do my best, sir. I pray to God that the dear young lady will open her eyes soon."

Turning to his companion, he said, "Joe, run for some water, and tell my Mrs. to come as quick as she can to Lady Anne." He scrambled into the saddle and, with a "Giddyup" and a clap on my sides with both his legs, started on his journey, making a little circuit to avoid the dike.

He had no whip, but my pace made a whip unnecessary. He found that the best thing he could do was to stick to the saddle and hold me in, which he did manfully. I shook him as little as I could, but once or twice on the rough ground he called out, "Steady! Whoa! Steady!" On the high road we were fine. At Dr. Ashley's and at Earlshall, the man did his errands.

At Earlshall the news of Lady Anne's fall caused much hurry and excitement. I was turned into my stall, my saddle and bridle were removed, and a cloth was thrown over me.

Ginger was saddled in great haste for Lord Gerald's son, Lord George, who rode off on her. Soon I also heard the carriage roll out of the yard.

It seemed a long time before Ginger came back and before we were left alone. Then she told me everything that she'd seen and heard. "I galloped nearly the whole way and got there just as the doctor rode up," she said. A woman was sitting on the ground with Lady Anne's head in her lap. The doctor said, 'Thank God, she's alive,' and poured something into Lady Anne's mouth. Then a man led me off a little distance. After a while the carriage arrived. Lady Anne was taken to it, and Lord George and I came home. A gentleman had stopped by to inquire about Lady Anne. Lord George told him that she didn't seem to have broken any bones but she hadn't spoken yet."

Two days after the accident, Colonel Blantyre paid me a visit. He patted me and praised me. He said to Lord George, "I'm sure he knew of Anne's danger as well as I did. I couldn't have held him in if I'd wanted to. Anne never should ride any other horse." Their conversation revealed that Lady Anne now was out of danger and soon would be able to ride again. This was good news to me. I looked forward to a happy life.

CHAPTER 25

Reuben Smith

W hen York went to London, Reuben Smith was left in charge of the stables. Max told me about Smith. Years before, Smith had been expected to drive a group home from a ball but had been too drunk to hold the reins. A gentleman in the group had mounted the driver's seat and driven the group home. Smith had been fired, and his family had been evicted from the pretty cottage by the park gate. Shortly before Ginger and I came, Smith had been rehired. York had interceded for him with Lord Gerald, and Smith had promised that he'd never taste another drop of alcohol as long as he lived at Earlshall. So far, Smith had kept his promise.

Smith was gentle and knowledgeable in his management of horses. He could doctor them almost as well as a veterinarian because he had lived with a veterinarian for two years. A first-rate driver, Smith could drive a four-in-hand or a tandem as easily as a pair. He was a handsome, intelligent man with pleasant manners. I think everyone liked him. The horses certainly did.

It now was early April. The light four-wheel carriage was to be refurbished before the family returned some time in May. Because Colonel Blantyre had to return to his regiment, it was arranged that Smith would drive him to the train station in the carriage, leave the carriage at the carriage maker's, and then ride back. I was chosen for the journey.

At the station Colonel Blantyre put some money into Smith's hand and bid him goodbye. "Take care of Lady Anne, and don't let Black Auster be driven or ridden by anyone careless. Keep him for Lady Anne."

After we left the carriage at the carriage maker's, Smith rode me to the White Lion and ordered the hostler to feed me well and have me ready for him at four o'clock.

A nail in one of my front shoes had loosened, but the hostler didn't notice this until about four o'clock. Smith didn't come into the yard until five. Then he said he wouldn't be leaving until six because he'd met up with some old friends. The hostler told Smith about the nail and asked if he should have the shoe fixed.

"No," Smith said. "It'll be all right until we get home." He spoke in a loud, offhand way. I thought it was very unlike him not to see about the shoe. Usually he was very particular about loose nails in our shoes.

Smith didn't come at six, seven, or eight. It was almost nine o'clock before he came for me. He was drunk and in a bad temper. He verbally abused the hostler.

The landlord stood at the door and said, "Watch yourself, Mr. Smith!"

Smith answered angrily with a curse.

Almost before we were out of town, we began to gallop. Although I was going at full speed, Smith frequently gave me a sharp cut with his whip. The moon hadn't risen yet, and it was very dark. The roads were stony, having been recently mended. Because I went over them at a fast pace, my shoe became looser. As we neared the turnpike gate, the shoe came off.

If Smith had been in his right senses, he would have noticed something wrong in my pace, but he was too drunk. Beyond the turnpike was a long road newly laid with fresh stones—large, sharp stones over which no horse could be driven quickly without danger. I was forced to gallop over this road at my utmost speed with one shoe gone. Smith kept cutting into me with his whip. With wild curses he urged me to go still faster.

My shoeless foot suffered terribly. My hoof split down to the very quick, and the sharp stones badly cut up the inside of my hoof. I couldn't keep my footing. The pain was too great. I stumbled and violently fell onto both my knees.

Smith was flung off by my fall. Because I was going at high speed, he fell with considerable force.

I soon recovered my feet and limped to the side of the road, where it was free of stones. The moon had just risen above the hedge. By its light I could see Smith lying a few yards from me. He didn't rise. He made one slight effort to rise and groaned heavily. I could have groaned, too, because I felt intense pain in my foot and knees. But horses usually bear their pain in silence. Smith gave another heavy groan. He lay motionless in the moonlight. I couldn't do anything for him or myself.

I listened for the sound of a horse, wheels, or footsteps. The road wasn't frequented. At that time of night it might be hours before someone came who could help us. I stood watching and listening. It was a calm, sweet night. There were no sounds except a few low notes of a nightingale. Nothing moved except the white clouds near the moon and a brown owl who flitted over the hedge. I was reminded of long-ago spring nights when I used to lie beside my mother in Farmer Grey's pleasant green meadow.

CHAPTER 26

How It Ended

It must have been nearly midnight when I heard a horse's feet at a distance. The road to Earlshall led through woods that belonged to Lord Gerald. The sound came from that direction, and I hoped it might be someone coming in search of us. As the sound neared, I thought I could distinguish Ginger's step. After some time I could tell that she was pulling the two-seat cart. I neighed loudly and was overjoyed to hear an answering neigh from Ginger, as well as men's voices.

Then the two-seat cart was visible. Robert and Ned, two of Lord Gerald's men, were in it. The cart came slowly over the stones and stopped at the body that lay on the ground.

Robert jumped out and stooped over the body. "It's Reuben," he said. "He doesn't stir!"

Ned followed and bent over Smith. "He's dead. Feel how cold his hands are."

Robert and Ned lifted the body. Smith's hair was soaked with blood. They laid the body down again and came and looked at me. They soon saw my cut knees.

"Why, the horse has been down and thrown him!" Robert said. "Who would have thought the black horse would do that? Reuben must've been lying here for hours! It's odd that the horse hasn't moved from the spot." Robert attempted to lead me forward. I took a step but almost fell again. "Look! His foot is hurt. His hoof is cut to pieces. Poor fellow! No wonder he fell. Reuben must have been drunk. Why else would he ride a horse over these stones without a shoe? What should we do? We have to get the horse home as well as the body."

Robert and Ned discussed the situation and agreed that Robert would lead me and Ned would take the body. It was hard to get the body into the cart. Ginger waited patiently, standing still. Ned started off slowly with the body.

Robert came and looked at my foot again. He bound it tightly with his handkerchief and led me home. I'll never forget that night walk. It was more than three miles. Robert led me very slowly. I limped and hobbled in great pain. I know that Robert felt sorry for me. He patted and encouraged me, talking to me in a pleasant voice.

At last I reached my stall and had some corn. After Robert wrapped my knees in wet cloths, he tied my foot in a bran poultice, to draw out the heat and cleanse it before the horse doctor saw it in the morning. I managed to get myself down onto the straw, and I slept in spite of the pain.

The next day the horse doctor examined my wounds and said that he hoped my knee joints weren't injured. If they weren't, I still could work. But, he said, I never would lose the blemish.

I believe the horse doctor and others did their best, but my recovery was slow and painful. The flesh around my knee wounds became so swollen with granulation tissue that the tissue had to be burned away with caustic. When my wounds finally healed, a blistering fluid was put on the front of both knees to remove all the hair. I don't know why.

Because Smith's death was so sudden, and no one had been there to see it, an inquest was held. The White Lion's landlord and hostler and several other people testified that Smith had been drunk when he left the inn. The keeper of the toll gate reported that Smith had ridden through the gate at a hard gallop. My shoe was found among the stones. The situation was plain to everyone. I was cleared of all blame.

CHAPTER 27

Ruined and
Going Downhill

As soon as my knees were sufficiently healed, I was turned into a small meadow for a month. No one else was there. Although I enjoyed the liberty and the sweet grass, I felt very lonely. Ginger and I had become close friends. I greatly missed her company. I often neighed when I heard horses' feet passing in the road, but I seldom got an answer.

Finally, one morning Ginger neighed back. The gate opened, and there she was. The man slipped off her halter and left her there. With a joyful whinny I trotted up to her. We were overjoyed to see each other, but I soon found that she'd been brought to the meadow for needed rest. She'd been ruined by hard riding.

Lord George was young and wouldn't heed any warning. He was a hard rider and would hunt whenever he had the chance, careless of his horse. Soon after I had left the stable, there had been a steeplechase. Although the groom had told Lord George that Ginger was strained and unfit for the race, Lord George had made her race and had continually urged her to keep up with the foremost riders. With her high spirit, she had strained herself to the utmost. She had come in with the first three horses, but her breathing had been affected. Also, Lord George was too heavy for her, so her back had been strained.

"So here we are," she said, "ruined in the prime of our youth and strength—you by a drunkard and I by a fool. It's very hard."

We both felt that we weren't what we'd been before. We didn't gallop around as we once had, but we enjoyed eating and lying down together. We would stand for hours under one of the shady lime trees with our heads close. And so we passed the time until the family returned from London.

One day Lord Gerald came into the meadow. York was with him. Ginger and I stood still under our lime tree and let them come up to us. They examined us carefully.

Lord Gerald was annoyed. "That's three hundred pounds flung away," he said. "But what bothers me most is that my old friend Squire Gordon thought these horses would have a good home with me. Instead, they've been ruined. The mare will have a year of rest, and we'll see what that does for her. But the black one must be sold. It's a great pity, but I couldn't have knees like his in my stables."

"No, my lord, of course not," York said, "but he might get a place where appearance doesn't matter much and he'll still be treated well. I know a man in Bath, the master of some livery stables, who often wants a good horse at a low price. He gives his horses good care. The inquest cleared the horse's character, and your lordship's recommendation or mine would suffice."

"Write to him, York. I care more about the quality of the place than the money that the sale will bring."

They left.

"They'll take you away soon," Ginger said. "I'll lose my only friend. Most likely, we'll never see each other again. How cruel!"

About a week later Robert came into the field with a halter, slipped it over my head, and led me away. I didn't have a chance to really say goodbye to Ginger. We neighed to each other as I was led off, and she trotted anxiously along the hedge, calling to me as long as she could hear the sound of my feet.

CHAPTER 28

A Job Horse

Through York's recommendation the master of the livery stables bought me. I had to go by train, which was new and frightening to me. When I realized that the puffing, rushing, and whistling of the train and, most of all, the shaking of my stall did me no harm, I accepted the situation quietly.

At the end of my journey, I found myself in a fairly comfortable stable and well attended to. This stable wasn't as airy and pleasant as the ones I was used to. The stalls were sloped instead of level. Because my head was kept tied to a manger, I always had to stand on the slope. This was very tiring. Humans don't seem to know that horses can do more work if they can stand comfortably and turn around.

However, I was well-fed and well cleaned. On the whole I think our master took as much care of his horses as he could. He kept many horses and carriages for hire. Sometimes his own men drove them. At other times the horse and carriage were rented to gentlemen or ladies who drove themselves.

Until now I'd always been driven by people who knew how to drive. However, in this place I experienced all the different kinds of bad and ignorant driving to which horses are subjected. I was a "job horse," rented to anyone who wanted to use me. I think I was rented to ignorant drivers more often than some of the other horses because I was gentle and dependable.

The tight-rein drivers thought that they must hold the reins as hard as they could, never relaxing their pull on my mouth or giving me the least freedom of movement. Some poor, broken-down horses whose mouths have been made hard and insensible by such drivers might find some support in tight reining. However, for easily guided horses with tender mouths, tight reining is stupid and tormenting.

The loose-rein drivers allowed the reins to lie on my back and lazily rested their hand on their knee. Such people have no control over a horse. If a horse starts or stumbles, they can't help the horse or themselves until the harm has been done. I didn't mind loose reining because I wasn't in the habit of starting or stumbling; I depended on a driver only for guidance and encouragement. Still, horses like to feel the rein a little when they go downhill and like to know that their driver hasn't fallen asleep. Besides, slovenly driving gets horses into bad and often lazy habits. When such horses change hands, they're whipped out of those habits. Squire Gordon always kept horses to their best paces and best manners. He said that spoiling a horse and letting them get into bad habits was as cruel as spoiling a child and that both suffered for it afterward. Loose-rein drivers often are completely careless. They'll attend to anything other than their horses.

One day I went out in a light, open four-wheel carriage with a loose-rein driver. A lady and two children sat behind him. The driver flopped the reins about as we started and gave me several unintended cuts with the whip. Much road repair was underway; there were many loose stones even where the stones weren't freshly laid. My driver laughed and joked with the lady and children, talking about the countryside views to the right and left. He never kept an eye on me or drove on the road's smoothest parts, so I got a stone in one of my forefeet.

If Squire Gordon, John, or any other good driver had been there, they would have seen that something was wrong before I'd gone three paces. Even in the dark a practiced hand would have felt, through the rein, that something was wrong in my step. They would have gotten down and picked out the stone. But this man kept laughing and talking while the stone became more firmly wedged between my shoe and sole. The stone was sharp on the inside and round on the outside. It cut my foot and made me likely to stumble and fall. The man drove me with that stone in my foot for a good half mile, until I went so lame from the pain that he noticed.

Then he called out, "Look at this! They've sent us out with a lame horse!" He jerked the reins and flicked the whip, saying, "We have a journey to make. It's no use turning lame and lazy on me."

A farmer came riding up on a stocky, short-legged brown horse. He lifted his hat and pulled up. "Excuse me, sir, but I think there's something wrong with your horse. He moves as if he has a stone in his shoe. If you'll allow me, I'll look at his feet. These loose, scattered stones are dangerous for the horses."

"He's a hired horse," my driver said. "I don't know what's wrong with him, but it's a great shame to send out a lame horse."

The farmer dismounted and, slipping his rein over his arm, immediately lifted my near foot. "There's a stone!" He tried to dislodge it with his hand, but it was tightly wedged. He drew a stone-pick from his pocket and carefully removed the stone. Holding it up, he said, "That's the stone your horse picked up. It's a wonder he didn't fall down and break his knees."

"What an odd thing," my driver said. "I never knew that horses pick up stones."

"You didn't?" the farmer said somewhat contemptuously. "Well, they do, including the best of them. They can't help it on roads like these. If you don't want to lame your horse, you need to keep a lookout and remove any stones right away. This horse's foot is badly bruised now," he said, setting it down gently and patting me. "I advise you to drive him gently. His lameness won't go away immediately." Mounting his horse and raising his hat to the lady, the farmer trotted off.

When he was gone, my driver flopped the reins about and whipped the harness, by which I understood that I was to go on. I was glad that the stone was gone but still in much pain. Job horses often have this sort of experience.

There also were steam-engine-style drivers, mostly townspeople who never had owned a horse and usually traveled by train. Such drivers think that a horse is like a steam engine, only smaller. To them a horse is bound to go as far, as fast, and with as heavy a load as they please. Whether the roads are muddy or dry, stony or smooth, uphill or downhill, it's all the same to them: go, go, go, with no relief or consideration for the horse. These people never think of getting out to walk up a steep hill. No, they've paid to ride. The horses? Oh, they're used to it. What are horses for if not to drag people uphill? So these drivers apply the whip, jerk the rein, and scold, "Go along, you lazy beast!" Another slash of the whip follows, even though the horse—downhearted, abused, but uncomplaining and obedient—is making every effort to move. Steam-engine driving wears horses down faster than any other kind. I'd rather go twenty miles with a good, considerate driver than go ten with a steam-engine driver. It takes less out of me.

Steam-engine drivers rarely apply the brake, however steep the downhill slope, so bad accidents sometimes occur. If the drivers do apply the brake, they often forget to take it off at the bottom of the hill. More than once I've had to pull halfway up the next hill with one of the wheels held by the brake before my driver thought about releasing the brake. That's a terrible strain on a horse.

Instead of starting at an easy pace, steam-engine drivers usually set off at full speed right from the stable yard. When they want to stop, they pull up so suddenly that horses are nearly thrown onto their haunches and the bit cuts their mouth. Steam-engine drivers turn corners as sharply as if there were no right and wrong sides of the road.

CHAPTER 29

My Companions

One spring evening Rory and I had been out for the day. Rory was the horse who usually went with me when a pair was ordered. He was a good, honest fellow. We had our own driver. He always was considerate and gentle, so we had a pleasant day.

About twilight we were coming home at a good pace. Our road turned sharply to the left. Because we stayed close to the hedge on our own side and there was plenty of room for passing, our driver didn't pull us in. As we neared the corner, I heard a horse and two wheels coming rapidly down the hill. The hedge was high, so I couldn't see anything. The next moment we saw a gig coming straight toward us. The driver didn't have time to pull over to his own side.

Luckily for me, I was on the side next to the hedge. Rory, who was on the left side of the pole, took the whole shock. The gig's shaft ran into his chest, making him stagger back with a cry that I'll never forget. The other horse was thrown onto his haunches. It turned out that he was a horse from our own stables, hitched to the high-wheel gig that the young men liked so much. The driver was one of those careless, ignorant fellows who don't care which side of the road they're on.

Poor Rory had his flesh torn open. Blood streamed down. If the blow had been a little more to one side, it would have killed him. It would have been better for him if the accident *had* killed him.

The wound took a long time to heal. Then Rory was sold to cart coal up and down steep hills. I've seen horses forced to go downhill with heavily loaded two-wheel carts behind them, carts with no brakes. It makes me sad to think about it.

After Rory was injured, I often was hitched to the carriage with a mare named Peggy, who stood in the stall next to mine. She was strong, well-built, grayish brown, beautifully dappled, with a dark brown mane and tail. She wasn't thoroughbred, but she was pretty and sweet-tempered. Still, there was an anxious look in her eyes.

The first time that Peggy and I went out together, I thought she had an odd pace. She would partly trot, partly canter. She'd go three or four paces and then give a little jump forward. It was very unpleasant for any horse who pulled with her and made me fidgety. When we got home, I asked her what made her go in that odd, awkward way.

"I know my paces are bad," Peggy said sadly. "It's because my legs are so short. I stand nearly as high as you, but your legs are a good three inches longer than mine. You can take a much longer step and go much faster. I have trouble keeping up. If I don't keep up, I get whipped. So I've developed this awkward shuffling pace. When I lived with my first master, I always went at a good regular trot because he wasn't in a hurry. He was a young clergyman in the country and a good, kind master. He had two churches a good distance apart and a great deal of work, but he never scolded or whipped me for not going faster. He was very fond of me. I wish I were with him now. He had to leave and go to a large town, and he sold me to a farmer. Some farmers are excellent masters, but this one was a low sort of man. He didn't care about good horses or good driving. He cared only about going fast. I went as fast as I could, but it wasn't good enough. He always was whipping me. So I developed this habit of springing forward to keep up. On market nights he'd stay very late at the inn and then drive home at a gallop. One dark night when he was making me gallop home, one of the gig's wheels suddenly hit something heavy and large in the road. The gig turned over, and he was thrown out. His arm and some of his ribs were broken. That was the end of my living with him, and I was glad."

Poor Peggy! I couldn't comfort her because I knew how hard it is on slow-paced horses to be put with fast ones. They keep getting whipped, although they can't go any faster.

Peggy often was used in the light, open four-wheel carriage. Some of the ladies liked her a lot because she was so gentle. Some time after this, she was sold to two ladies who drove themselves and wanted a good, safe horse.

Several times, I saw Peggy out in the country going at a good steady pace and looking happy. I was very glad to see her so happy. She deserved a good place.

After Peggy left us, another horse came: Dapper. He was young and had lost a good place because he had a habit of shying and starting. I asked him what made him shy.

"I don't really know," he said. "I've always been timid. When I was young, I was badly frightened a few times. If I saw anything strange, I'd turn and look at it. With blinders on we can't see or understand something unless we turn to look at it. My master would whip me for looking, which only made me more afraid. I think that if he had let me look at things and see that there wasn't anything to hurt me, I'd have gotten used to things and been all right. One day an old gentleman was riding with my master, and a large piece of white paper blew across on one side of me. I shied and started forward. As usual my master whipped me smartly. The old man cried out, 'You're wrong! You never should whip horses for shying. They shy because they're afraid. Whipping them only makes them more afraid.' I don't *want* to shy when there's nothing to be afraid of. But how am I supposed to know what's dangerous and what isn't if I'm never allowed to look? I don't shy from familiar things. Many horses shy and kick when they see a deer. I don't, because I was brought up in a park where there were deer."

I knew that what Dapper said was true. I wished that every young horse had as good a master as Farmer Grey or Squire Gordon.

CHAPTER 30

A Thief

One morning I was hitched to the gig and taken to a house in Pulteney Street. Two gentlemen came out. The taller one came around to my head. He looked at the bit and bridle and shifted the collar with his hand to see if it fit comfortably.

"Does this horse need a curb?" he asked the hostler.

"No," the man answered. "He has an uncommon good mouth, and although he has a fine spirit, he has no vice. Still, we find that people usually like the curb."

"I don't like it," the gentleman said. "Please remove it and put the rein in at the cheek. A comfortable mouth is a great thing on a long journey, isn't it, old fellow?" he said to me, patting my neck. He took the reins, and they both got up. After the gentleman quietly turned me, he held the rein lightly and drew the whip gently across my back, and we were off.

I arched my neck and set off at my best pace. I had someone behind me who knew how a good horse should be driven. It seemed like old times again and made me feel happy.

The gentleman took a great liking to me. After trying me several times with a saddle, he persuaded my master to sell me to a friend of his who wanted a safe, pleasant horse for riding. So in the summer I was sold to Mr. Barry.

Barry was a bachelor who lived in Bath and was much engaged in business. His doctor had advised him to take horse exercise, and he bought me for this purpose. He rented a stable a short distance from his lodgings and hired a man named Filcher as a groom. Barry knew very little about horses, but he treated me well. He ordered the best hay with plenty of oats, crushed beans, and bran.

For a few days everything went well. Filcher understood his business. He kept the stable clean and airy, and he groomed me thoroughly and always was gentle. He'd been a hostler in one of Bath's fine hotels, but he'd given that up. He now grew fruits and vegetables for the market. His wife bred and fattened chickens, geese, and rabbits for sale.

After a while my supply of oats was inadequate. I had beans and bran but hardly any oats. Within about two weeks, the lack of oats began to weaken me and lower my spirits. The grass food, though good, wasn't enough to maintain my condition without corn. Of course, I had no way of telling Barry. This continued for about two months, and I wondered that Barry didn't notice that something was wrong.

One afternoon Barry rode out into the country to see a friend, a gentleman farmer. This gentleman had a quick eye for horses. After welcoming Barry, he looked at me. "Barry," he said, "your horse doesn't look as healthy as when you bought him. Has he been ill?"

"I don't think so," Barry answered, "but he isn't nearly as lively as he was. My groom says that horses always are dull and weak in the autumn."

"Dull and weak in the autumn! What nonsense! With light work and good food, this horse should look a lot better than this. What do you feed him?"

Barry told him.

The farmer shook his head slowly and began to feel me over. "I can't say who eats the oats, Barry, but I'm quite sure your horse doesn't. Have you ridden very fast?"

"No, very gently."

"Put your hand here," the farmer said, passing his hand over my neck and shoulder. "He's warm and damp. I fear that some scoundrel is robbing dumb beasts of their food. I advise you to look into it." Turning to his stableman, who had come to take me, the farmer said, "Give this horse a generous supply of oats."

"Dumb beasts!" If I'd been able to speak, I could have told Barry where his oats were going. Every morning at about six o'clock, Filcher would come in with his small son, who always held a covered basket. They'd go into the harness room, where the oats were kept, and fill a bag with oats from the bin. When the door was ajar, I'd see them do it. Then the boy would leave with the oats.

About a week later, as the boy was leaving the stable, the door was pushed open and a policeman walked in. He grabbed the child by his arm. Another policeman followed and locked the door on the inside, saying, "Show me where your father keeps his rabbit food."

The boy looked frightened and started to cry, but he led the way to the oats bin. Here the policeman found another empty bag like the one, filled with oats, in the boy's basket.

Filcher was cleaning my feet at the time, but the policemen soon saw him. Although he blustered a lot, they walked him off to prison, along with his boy. I heard afterward that the boy wasn't held to be guilty, but Filcher was sentenced to two months in prison.

CHAPTER 31

A Humbug

My new groom, Alfred Smirk, came a few days later. He was a tall, good-looking man. He never abused me. In fact, whenever Barry was present, Smirk would stroke and pat me a lot. To make me look smart, he always brushed my mane and tail with water and my hoofs with oil before he brought me to the door. However, he never thoroughly groomed me, cleaned my feet, or attended to my shoes. He left my bit rusty, my saddle damp, and my crupper stiff.

Smirk spent much of his time fixing his hair, whiskers, and necktie while standing before a small mirror in the harness room. When Barry spoke to him, Smirk always responded, "Yes, sir" and politely touched his hat, so everyone thought that he was a nice young man and that Barry was lucky to have him. In my opinion, Smirk was the laziest, most conceited fellow I'd ever met.

I had a loose stall and might have been very comfortable if Smirk hadn't been too lazy to clean it out. He never removed all the straw, so the smell from what lay underneath was foul. The strong vapors made my eyes smart and become inflamed. My appetite decreased.

One day Barry came in and said, "Alfred, the stable has a strong smell. Shouldn't you give that stall a good scrub?"

Touching his cap, Smirk said, "I'll do that if you want me to, sir, but it's rather dangerous to wash out a horse's stall. Horses are apt to take cold. I wouldn't want to injure him."

"I don't want him to take cold, but I don't like this stable's smell. Do you think the drains are all right?"

"Now that you mention it, the drain does sometimes send back a smell. There might be something wrong, sir."

"Send for the bricklayer, and have it seen to."

"Yes, sir."

The bricklayer came and pulled up many bricks but found nothing wrong, so he put down some lime and charged Barry five shillings. The smell in my stall remained foul.

Because I had to stand on moist straw, my feet became unhealthy and sore. Barry would say, "I don't know what's wrong with this horse. He goes very fumble-footed. Sometimes I'm afraid that he'll stumble."

"Yes, sir," Smirk said. "I've noticed that, too, when I've exercised him."

Smirk hardly ever exercised me. When Barry was busy, I often stood for days without stretching my legs at all, yet I was fed as much as I would have been if I had been working hard. The combination of lack of exercise and overfeeding damaged my health. Sometimes I felt heavy and dull. More often I felt restless and feverish. Smirk never fed me green food or a bran mash, which would have cooled me. He was as ignorant as he was conceited. Instead of exercise or the proper food, I was given medicine, which was poured down my throat and made me feel ill.

One day my feet were so sore that I seriously stumbled twice while trotting over some fresh stones with Barry on my back. Barry stopped at the farrier's and asked him to see what was wrong with me. The farrier took up my feet one by one and examined them. Then, standing up and dusting his hands one against the other, he said, "Your horse has a bad case of infected feet. I'm surprised he hasn't been down. Your groom should have seen to this. This is the sort of thing we find in foul stables, where the litter never is properly cleaned out. If you'll send your groom here tomorrow, I'll attend to the hoofs and show him how to apply the liniment that I'll give him."

The next day I had my feet thoroughly cleansed and stuffed with tow soaked in strong lotion. It was an unpleasant business. The farrier instructed that all litter be removed from my stall every day and that the floor be kept clean. I was to have bran mashes, a little green food, and less corn until my feet healed. With this treatment I soon regained my spirits.

Barry was so disgusted at having twice been deceived by grooms that he decided to stop having a horse and to rent one whenever he needed one. So when my feet were well, I was sold again.

CHAPTER 32

A Horse Fair

I suppose that those who have nothing to lose find a horse fair entertaining. There's plenty to see: long strings of young horses fresh from the countryside; droves of shaggy little Welsh ponies no higher than Merrylegs; hundreds of cart horses of all kinds, some of them with their long tails braided and tied with scarlet ribbon; many thoroughbreds, such as myself, whose financial value has been reduced by some accident or ailment.

There were some splendid horses in their prime, fit for anything. They threw out their legs and showed off their paces in high style as they were trotted out with a leading rein, the groom running by their side. But in the background were a number of poor creatures, broken down from hard work, their knees knuckling over and their hind legs swinging out at every step. There were some very sad-looking old horses with their lower lip hanging down and their ears lying back heavily, indicating that life offered them no more pleasure or hope. Some horses were so thin that the outline of their ribs was visible. Some had old sores on their backs and hips. I wondered if I would come to the same end.

There was much bargaining. I believe that many lies were told at that horse fair.

I was put with several other strong, useful-looking horses, and many people came to look at us. The gentlemen always turned from me when they saw my scarred knees, although the man offering me for sale swore that I only had slipped in my stall.

Prospective buyers pulled my mouth open, looked at my eyes, felt all the way down my legs, felt my skin and flesh, and tried my paces. Some did all these things roughly, as if I were a piece of wood or other inanimate object. Others put their hands gently over my body, with a periodic pat that seemed to say, "Excuse me for doing this."

I could tell a lot about the buyers from the way they handled me. There was one man I wanted to buy me. He wasn't a gentleman or the loud, flashy kind of man who thinks he's a gentleman. He was a rather small, well-built man, quick in all his movements. I knew in a moment that he was used to horses. He spoke gently. His gray eyes had a kindly, cheerful look.

He didn't smell of beer or tobacco—smells that I hate. Instead he had a clean, fresh smell as if he'd come out of a hayloft. He offered twenty-three pounds for me, but that was refused. I looked after him as he walked away.

A very hard-looking, loud-voiced man came next. I was terribly afraid that he'd buy me. He walked off but soon came back and offered twenty-three pounds. My salesman began to think that he wouldn't get the amount he'd originally asked for and that he must come down in his price.

Just then the gray-eyed man returned. I reached out my head toward him. He stroked my face. "Well, old chap," he said, "I think we'd suit each other. I'll pay twenty-four for him."

"Say twenty-five, and you'll have him."

"Twenty-four ten," my friend said in a decided tone. "Not another sixpence. Yes or no?"

"Done," the salesman said. "There's a lot of quality in that horse. If you want him for cab work, he's a bargain."

The money was paid on the spot. My new master took my halter and led me out of the fair to an inn, where he had a saddle and bridle ready. He gave me a good meal of oats and stood by while I ate, talking to himself and to me.

Half an hour later we were on our way to London. We passed through pleasant lanes and country roads until we came to the great

London thoroughfare, on which we traveled steadily.

At twilight we reached the city. The gas lamps were lit. There were streets to the right, streets to the left, and streets crossing each other, mile after mile. I thought we'd never reach the end of them.

At last we turned up a side street. About halfway up that, we turned into a narrow street with poor-looking houses on one side and coach houses and stables on the other.

My owner pulled up at one of the houses and whistled. The door flew open, and a young woman ran out, followed by a little girl and boy. There were lively greetings as my rider dismounted.

"Harry, my boy, open the gates. Mother will bring us the lantern."

The next minute, they all were standing around me in a small stable yard.

"Is he gentle, Father?"

"Yes, Dolly, as gentle as your kitten. Come pat him."

At once the little hand was patting all over my shoulder. How good it felt!

"Let me get him a bran mash while you rub him down," the mother said.

"Do, Polly. It's just what he needs. I know you've got a beautiful mash ready for *me*."

"Sausage dumpling and apple turnover!"

the boy said, making all of them laugh.

I was led into a comfortable, clean-smelling stall with plenty of dry straw. After an excellent supper, I lay down, thinking, "I'm going to be happy here."

CHAPTER 33

A London Cab Horse

My new master was Jeremiah Barker. Everyone called him Jerry. Polly, his wife, was as good a match as a man could have. She was a plump, tidy little woman with dark eyes, a merry little mouth, and smooth, dark hair. Harry was twelve years old, a tall, frank, good-natured lad. Little Dolly was her mother all over again, at eight years old. They all were wonderfully fond of one another. I never knew such a happy family before or since.

Jerry had his own cab and two horses, whom he drove and attended to himself. His other horse was a tall, white, large-boned animal called Captain. He was old now, but he must have been splendid when he was young. He still had a proud way of holding his head and arching his neck. He was a thoroughbred, fine-mannered, noble old horse, every inch of him.

The next morning, when I was well-groomed, Polly and Dolly came into the yard to see me and make friends. Harry had been helping his father since early morning and had stated his opinion that I'd turn out to be a "great horse." Polly brought me a slice of apple. Dolly brought me a piece of bread and fussed over me as if I were the Black Beauty of earlier years. It was a great treat to be petted again and talked to in a gentle voice. I let the family see that I wanted to be friendly. Polly thought I was very handsome and much too good for a cab, except for my scarred knees.

"I bet that wasn't his fault," Jerry said. "I've never ridden a horse with a firmer, neater step. Shall we call him Jack after our old horse?"

"Yes, let's do that," Polly said. "I like to keep a good name going."

Captain went out in the cab all morning. Harry came in after school to feed me and give me water. In the afternoon I was hitched to the cab. Jerry was as careful as John Manly in seeing that my collar and bridle fit me comfortably. When the crupper was let out a hole or two, it all fit well. There wasn't any checkrein or curb, nothing but a plain ring bit. What a blessing that was!

After driving through the side street, we came to a wide street with a large cab stand. On one side of this street were high houses with wonderful shop fronts. On the other side was an old church with a yard surrounded by iron rails. A number of cabs were drawn up alongside these rails, waiting for passengers. Bits of hay lay about on the ground. Some of the men were standing together talking. Some were sitting on their driver's seat reading the newspaper. One or two were feeding their horses bits of hay and giving them a drink of water.

We pulled up behind the last cab. Several men came to look at me.

"Very good for a funeral," one said.

"Too smart-looking," another said, shaking his head. "One of these mornings you'll find there's something wrong with him."

Jerry said pleasantly, "I don't intend to find anything wrong until it finds *me*."

A broad-faced, gray-haired man dressed in a large gray coat, gray cape, and gray hat came up. His coat had large white buttons. A blue scarf was loosely tied around his neck. The other men made way for him. He looked me over carefully. Then he straightened himself and said, "He's the right sort of horse for you, Jerry. Whatever you paid for him, he'll be worth it." This man was Mr. Grant. Of all the men, he had been at the cab stand the longest. Cabmen went to him to settle disputes because he was fair, sensible, and good-hearted.

The first week of my life as a cab horse was

very trying. I wasn't used to London. The noise, the hurry, and the crowds of horses, carts, and carriages through which I had to make my way made me feel nervous and harassed. But I found that I could fully trust Jerry, so I soon calmed down and got used to the situation.

As good a driver as I'd ever known, Jerry showed his horses great consideration. He soon saw that I was willing to work and do my best. He never laid the whip on me except to gently draw its end over my back when I was to go on. Usually I knew this just from the way he took up the reins. His whip was stuck by his side more often than it was in his hand.

Jerry and I soon understood each other as well as a horse and human can. In the stable he did everything he could to make me comfortable. Captain's stall and mine were old-fashioned, too sloped, but Jerry put two removable bars across the back of them. At night and when Captain and I were resting during the day, Jerry would take off our halters and remove the bars. That way we could turn about and stand however we wanted to, which was a great comfort.

Jerry kept Captain and me very clean. He gave us abundant, varied food. He always gave us plenty of clean, fresh water, which he left by us night and day except when we came in warm. Some people say that horses shouldn't be allowed to drink as much as they like. But I know that when we have free access to water, we drink only a little at a time. That's much healthier than swallowing half a bucketful because we've been left thirsty. Some grooms will go home to their beer and leave horses for hours with dry hay and oats and nothing to moisten them. Then, of course, the horses gulp down too much water when they're finally given some. This can chill their stomachs and permanently impair their breathing.

The best thing that Captain and I had with Jerry was our Sundays of rest. We worked so hard during the rest of the week that I don't think we could have kept up if we hadn't been allowed to rest on Sundays. On Sundays Captain and I had time to enjoy each other's company.

CHAPTER 34

An Old War Horse

Captain had been broken in and trained to be an army horse. His first owner was a cavalry officer who fought in the Crimean War. Captain said that he enjoyed being trained with all the other army horses. They trotted together, turned to the right and left together, halted at the word of command, or dashed forward at the sound of the trumpet or the officer's signal.

When young, Captain was a dark, dappled iron-gray and considered very handsome. His master, a young, high-spirited gentleman, was very fond of him and always treated him with the greatest care and kindness.

Captain found the life of an army horse very pleasant except when he was sent over the sea in a great ship. "That part was dreadful!" Captain said. "To get us onto the ship, they put strong straps under our bodies, lifted us off our legs, and swung us through the air over the water, to the deck of the great vessel. There we were placed in small, close stalls. For a long time we didn't see the sky or stretch our legs. The ship sometimes rolled about in high winds, and we were knocked about and felt sick. But the voyage finally ended. We were hauled up and swung over to the land. When we felt firm ground under our feet again, we snorted and neighed for joy. We soon found that the country we'd come to was very different from England and that we had to endure many hardships besides fighting. But many of the men were so fond of their horses that they did everything they could to make them comfortable in spite of cold, wet, and disorder."

"What about the fighting?" I asked. "Wasn't that worse than anything else?"

"We horses always liked to hear the trumpet sound and to be called out. We were impatient to start off, although sometimes we had to stand for hours, waiting for the word of command. When the word was given, we'd spring forward as eagerly as if there were no cannon balls, bayonets, or bullets. As long as we felt our rider firm in the saddle and his hand steady on the bridle, none of us gave way to fear, not even when the bombshells whirled through the air and burst into a thousand pieces.

"My noble master and I went into many battles without being wounded. Although I saw horses shot down with bullets, pierced through with lances, and gashed with saber cuts— although we left them dead on the field or dying in the agony of their wounds—I didn't feel afraid. My master's cheerful voice, as he encouraged his men, made me feel that he and I couldn't be killed. I trusted him so much that when he guided me, I was ready to charge right up to the cannon's mouth. I saw many brave men be cut down, many fall mortally wounded from their saddles. I heard the cries and groans of the dying. I stepped over ground slippery with blood. Frequently I had to turn aside to avoid trampling a wounded man or horse. But I felt no terror until one dreadful day."

Captain paused and drew a long breath. I waited, and he went on. "One autumn morning our cavalry turned out, as usual, an hour before daybreak. Wearing our ornamental coverings, we were ready for the day's work, whether it be fighting or waiting. The men stood by their horses, waiting for their orders. As the daylight increased, there was some excitement among the officers.

"Before long we heard the enemy's guns firing. An officer rode up and gave the word for the men to mount. In a second every man was in his saddle. Every horse stood expecting the touch of the rein or the pressure of his rider's heels. We all were eager, but we'd been trained so well that we didn't stir except to champ our bits and restlessly toss our heads from time to time. My dear master and I were at the head of the line. As everyone sat motionless and watchful, he took a stray lock of my mane, which had turned over on the wrong side, laid it right, and smoothed it down with his hand. Patting my neck, he said, 'We'll have a rough day today, Bayard, my beauty. But we'll do our duty.' That morning he stroked my neck more than ever before—quietly, on and on. I loved to feel his hand on my neck. I arched my crest proudly and happily, but I stood very still because I knew from his mood that he wanted stillness.

"That day the battle was especially fierce. My master and I charged across a valley right in front of the enemy's cannon. We were used to the roar of heavy guns, the rattle of musket fire, and the flying of shot near us. But I'd never been under such heavy fire. Shot and shell poured on us from the right, left, and front. Many brave men went down. Many horses fell, flinging their rider to the earth. Many riderless horses ran wildly out of the ranks, then—terrified at being alone, with no hand to guide them—came pressing in among their old companions, to gallop with them to the charge. Terrifying as it was, no one stopped or turned back. Every moment, the ranks were thinned. As our comrades fell, we closed in to keep together. Instead of becoming shaky or hesitant, we galloped faster as we neared the cannon.

"My dear master was cheering on his comrades with his right arm raised high when one of the balls whizzing close to my head struck him. I felt him stagger from the shock, although he uttered no cry. I tried to check my speed, but the sword dropped from his right hand, the rein fell loose from his left hand, and, sinking backward from the saddle, he fell to earth. The other riders swept past us. The force of their charge drove me from the spot. I wanted to stay by my master's side and not leave him under the rush of horses' feet, but it was no use. Now, without a master or friend, I was alone on a great slaughter ground. Fear gripped me. I trembled as I'd never trembled before. I tried to join in the ranks and gallop with other horses, but soldiers' swords beat me off.

"Then a soldier whose horse had been killed grabbed my bridle and mounted me. With this new master I again went forward. But our gallant company was cruelly overpowered. Those who remained alive after the fierce fight came galloping back over the same ground. Some of the horses were so badly wounded that they scarcely could move because of blood loss. Other noble horses were trying to drag themselves on three legs. Others, their hind legs shattered, were struggling to rise onto their forefeet. After the battle the wounded men were brought in, and the dead were buried."

"What about the wounded horses?" I asked. "Were they left to die?"

"No. The horse doctors went over the field with their pistols and shot all of the horses who were ruined. Some horses who had only slight wounds were brought back and attended to, but most of the noble, willing horses who went out that morning never came back. In our stables only about one in four returned. I never saw my dear master again. I think he fell dead from the saddle. I've never loved another master as much as I loved him. I went into many other battles but was wounded only once, not seriously. When the war ended, I came back to England as sound and strong as when I'd left."

"I've heard people talk about war as if it were a very fine thing," I said.

"Ah!" Captain said. "They must never have seen it. No doubt it's very fine when there's no enemy, when it's just exercise, parade, and sham fight. But when thousands of good, brave men and horses are killed or crippled for life, it has a very different look."

"Do you know what they fought about?" I asked.

"No," he said. "That's more than a horse can understand. But the enemy must have been very wicked if it was right to go all that way over the sea to kill them."

CHAPTER 35

Jerry Barker

I never knew a better man than my new master. He was kind and good and as dedicated to standing up for what's right as John Manly. He was so good-tempered and merry that few people could pick a quarrel with him.

Harry was as good at stable work as a much older boy and always wanted to do what he could. Polly and Dolly would come in the morning to help with the cab. They'd brush and beat the cushions and rub the glass while Jerry cleaned Captain and me in the yard and Harry rubbed the harness. There was much laughing and fun within the family. It put Captain and me in good spirits.

Jerry couldn't bear any careless loitering and wasting of time. Nothing annoyed him more than people who always were late and wanted cab horses to be driven hard to make up for their lateness.

One day two wild-looking young men came out of a tavern near the cab stand and called Jerry. "Here, cabby! Look sharp. We're rather late. Hurry and take us to Victoria Station in time for the one o'clock train. You'll have a shilling extra."

"I'll take you at the regular pace, gentlemen. Shillings don't pay for hurrying like that."

Larry's cab was standing next to ours. Larry flung open the door and said, "I'm your man, gentlemen! Take my cab. My horse will get you there in time." As he shut the men in, Larry mockingly said of Jerry, "It's against his conscience to go beyond a trot." Slashing his worn-out horse, Larry set off as hard as he could.

Jerry patted me on the neck. "No, Jack, a shilling wouldn't pay for that sort of thing, would it, old boy?"

Although Jerry was against driving hard in order to please careless people, he wasn't against hurrying for a good reason. One morning as we were at the cab stand waiting for a fare, a young man carrying a heavy suitcase stepped on a piece of orange peel that lay on the pavement and fell down with great force.

Jerry ran and lifted him up. The young man seemed stunned. As people led him into a shop, he walked as if he were in great pain.

Jerry returned to the cab stand, but in about ten minutes one of the shop people called him, so we drew up to the pavement.

"Can you take me to the South-Eastern Railway?" the young man asked. "This fall has made me late. It's very important that I not miss the noon train. I'd be very grateful if you could get me there in time. I'll gladly pay you extra."

"I'll do my best, sir, if you think you're well enough," Jerry said.

The young man looked white and ill. "I must go," he said earnestly. "Please open the door. I mustn't lose any more time."

The next minute Jerry was on the driver's seat with a cheerful clucking sound to me and a twitch of the rein that I understood well. "Jack, my boy," he said, "spin along. We'll show them how we can hurry when we have a good reason to."

It's always difficult to drive fast in London at midday, when the streets are full of traffic, but we did what we could. When a good driver and good horse who understand each other are of one mind, it's wonderful what they can do. I had a very good mouth—I could be guided by the slightest touch of the rein—and that's important in London among carriages, buses, carts, vans, trucks, cabs, and wagons creeping along at a walking pace, some going one way, some another, some going slowly, others wanting to pass them.

Buses stop short every few minutes to pick up a passenger, forcing horses who are behind them to stop too or pass. If you try to pass and something else comes dashing in through the narrow opening, you have to get back behind the bus. Presently you see a chance of passing. You go so close to the wheels on each side of you that your cab would scrape them if they were half an inch closer. You go along for a while but soon find yourself in a long train of carts and carriages all obliged to go at walking pace. Perhaps you come to a traffic jam and have to stand still for minutes until something clears out into a side street or a policeman intervenes. You have to be ready for any chance—ready to dash forward if there's an opening, quick to judge whether you have enough space and time to avoid getting your wheels locked or smashed or having the shaft of some other vehicle run into your chest or shoulder. Getting through London quickly at midday takes a lot of practice.

Jerry and I were used to the maneuvering. No one could beat us at getting through when we were set on it. I was quick and bold and always could trust my driver. Jerry was quick yet patient, and he could trust his horse. He seldom used the whip. I knew from his voice and his click, click when he wanted to move fast, and I knew from the rein where I was supposed to go.

The streets were very full that day, but we got on pretty well as far as the bottom of Cheapside, where there was a jam for several minutes. The young man put his head out and said anxiously, "I think I'd better get out and walk. If this continues, I won't get there in time."

"I'll do all that can be done, sir," Jerry said. "I think we'll be there in time. This jam can't last much longer, and your suitcase is very heavy for you to carry."

Just then the cart in front of us began to move on. In and out we went, as fast as a horse and cab could. We had a good, clear time on London Bridge because a whole train of cabs and carriages was going our way at a quick trot. We whirled into the station just as the great clock pointed to eight minutes to twelve.

"Thank God! We're in time," the young man said. "Many thanks to you, my friend, and to your good horse. You've saved me more than money ever could pay for. Please take this extra half crown."

"No, sir. Thank you all the same. I'm glad we made it in time. Don't stay now. The bell is ringing. Here, porter! Take this gentleman's suitcase. Dover line, noon train. That's it." Without waiting for another word, Jerry wheeled me around to make room for other cabs that were dashing up at the last minute. We drew up on one side until the crush was over. "I'm glad he made it," Jerry said. "I wonder what made him so anxious."

When Jerry returned to the cab stand, there was much laughing and teasing of him for driving hard to the train for an extra-big fare—"against your principles," some men said.

"He's a hypocrite," one cabman said. "He preaches against hurrying and then does it himself."

"Look here, mates," Jerry said. "The gentleman offered me half a crown extra, but I didn't take it. It was enough reward for me to see how glad he was to catch his train. If Jack and I choose to have a quick run now and then for a good cause, that's our business."

"Well," Larry said, "you'll never be a rich man."

"Probably not," Jerry said, "but that doesn't mean I won't be a happy man. I've heard the Ten Commandments read many times, and I've never noticed that any of them say 'Thou shalt be rich.' The New Testament says many things about rich people that make me think I'd feel pretty uncomfortable being one of them."

Looking over his shoulder across the top of his cab, Mr. Grant said, "If you *do* ever get rich, you'll deserve it, Jerry, and you won't find that your wealth brings any curse. As for you, Larry, you'll die poor: you spend too much on whip cord."

Larry said, "What's a fellow to do if his horses won't go without being whipped?"

"You never bother to see if they'll go without it. Your whip is always going. If it doesn't wear you out, it wears your horses out. You're always changing your horses. Why? Because you never give them any peace or encouragement."

"I haven't had good luck," Larry said.

"And you never will," Mr. Grant said. "Good Luck is rather particular about who she rides with. Mostly she prefers those who have common sense and a good heart."

Mr. Grant turned back to his newspaper, and the other men went to their cabs.

CHAPTER 36

The Sunday Cab

One morning, after Jerry hitched me to the cab, a gentleman named Mr. Briggs walked into the yard.

"Good morning, Mr. Barker," Mr. Briggs said.

"Your servant, sir," Jerry responded, touching his cap.

"I'd like to arrange for you to take Mrs. Briggs to church on Sunday mornings. We go to the New Church now, and it's farther than she can walk."

"Thank you, sir, but my license doesn't include Sunday driving."

"Oh," Mr. Briggs said. "I didn't know that. Of course, you can easily get a seven-day license. I'd see to it that you profited from doing that. Mrs. Briggs would very much like you to drive her."

"I'd be glad to oblige, sir, but I had a seven-day license once, and the work was too hard for me and my horses. Year after year we never had a day's rest, and I never had a Sunday with my wife and children or was able to go to church. So for the past five years, I've had only a six-day license."

"Of course, it's proper that every person have rest and go to church on Sundays," Mr. Briggs said. "However, the distance would be short. You'd have the whole afternoon and evening for yourself. We're good customers, you know."

"Yes, sir, and I'm grateful for your business. I'd like to oblige Mrs. Briggs and you, but I can't give up my Sundays. God made people, horses, and all the other animals, and as soon as he finished, he made a day of rest and said that everyone should rest one day in seven. He must have known what's best for us. I'm stronger and healthier now that I have a day of rest. The horses are fresh, too, and don't wear out nearly as fast. Other six-day drivers say the same thing. I've put more money in the savings bank than ever before. As for my wife and children, they wouldn't want me to go back to seven working days."

"Very well," Mr. Briggs said. "I'll inquire somewhere else." And he walked away.

"Well," Jerry said to me, "we can't help it, Jack, old boy. We must have our Sundays." Then he shouted, "Polly!"

She was there in a minute. "What is it, Jerry?"

"Mr. Briggs wants me to take Mrs. Briggs to church every Sunday morning. I said that I have only a six-day license. He said if I get a seven-day license, he'll make it worth my while. They *have* been good customers. Mrs. Briggs often shops or visits people for hours, and then—unlike many people—she gladly gives me the full pay that's due me. And it's easy work for the horses, not like tearing along for people who are running late and have to catch a train. If I don't oblige Mr. and Mrs. Briggs in this, we'll probably lose them as customers. What do you think, Polly?"

Polly said, "I wouldn't have you be a seven-day cabman again even if Mrs. Briggs gave you a sovereign every Sunday. We know what it's like to have our Sundays free and what it's like not to have them. Although we sometimes have only enough money to pay for the oats and hay, the license, and the rent, you earn enough to provide for us. Harry soon will be earning something. I'd rather struggle more than we do now than go back to those horrid times when you hardly had a minute to look at your own children and we never could go to church together or have a quiet, happy day."

"That's just what I told Mr. Briggs, my dear," Jerry said.

Polly started to cry.

"Don't fret, Polly. I wouldn't go back to the

old times if I earned twice as much. It's settled. Cheer up. I'm off to the cab stand."

Three weeks passed with no order from Mrs. Briggs, so all of Jerry's jobs were from the cab stand. Jerry took this to heart because cab work was harder for us. But Polly always cheered him up, saying, "Never mind."

It soon became known that Jerry had lost his best customer, and why. Most of the men said he was a fool, but two or three agreed with him.

One cabman said, "Working men should stick to having their Sundays off. It's the right of every person and every animal. By God's law we have a day of rest and by England's law. I think we should hold to those rights."

"It's all right for you religious men to talk that way," Larry said, "but I'll earn a shilling when I can. I don't believe in religion. I don't think religious people are any better than others."

"If they aren't better, it's because they aren't truly religious," Jerry said. "You might as well say that our country's laws aren't good because some people break them. If people give way to their temper, speak evil of their neighbors, and don't pay their debts, they aren't religious, however much they go to church. If some people are phonies and hypocrites, that doesn't make religion untrue. Real religion is the best and truest thing in the world and the only thing that can make a person really happy or make the world any better."

"If religion was good for anything," another cabman said, "it would prevent religious people from making us work on Sundays by driving them to church. They get to go to church, and we don't. They don't care about anybody's precious soul but their own. Religion is a sham."

Several of the men applauded until Jerry said, "Every person must look after their own soul. You can't blame other people if you don't look after yours. If you're sitting on your cab waiting for a fare, of course people will use you. If you Sunday drivers would all strike for a day of rest, that would put an end to the matter."

"What would people do if they couldn't get to their favorite preachers?" Larry asked.

"If a place is too far to walk to, they can find a closer place," Jerry said. "If it rains, they can put on their raincoats as they do on weekdays. If a thing is right, a good person will find a way to do it. If a thing is wrong, it shouldn't be done. That's as true for us cabmen as for anyone else."

Several weeks later as we entered the yard rather late in the evening, Polly came running across the road with the lantern. "Great news, Jerry. Mrs. Briggs's servant came this afternoon. Mrs. Briggs would like you to take her out tomorrow at eleven. I said you'd be pleased to do that. The servant told me that Mr. Briggs was annoyed when you refused to drive on

Sundays, so Mrs. Briggs tried other cabs, but she found something wrong with all of them. Some drive too fast, some too slow. Mrs. Briggs says that none of them are as nice and clean as yours. She wants your cab again." Polly was almost out of breath.

Jerry laughed merrily. "That *is* great news, Polly. Run in and get supper. I'll have Jack's harness off and make him snug and happy in no time."

After this Mrs. Briggs wanted Jerry's cab as often as before.

CHAPTER 37

The Golden Rule

One Saturday night Jerry, Captain, and I came home very tired and very glad to think that the next day would be all rest. The next morning Jerry was cleaning me in the yard when Polly stepped up to him, looking troubled.

"What is it?" Jerry asked.

"Dinah Brown's mother is dying. Dinah must go immediately if she wants to see her mother alive. The place is more than ten miles from here, out in the country. Dinah says that if she takes the train, she'll have to walk four miles. She's weak because she gave birth only a month ago. She wants to know if you'll take her in your cab. She promises to pay you as soon as she has the money."

"I'm not worried about the money," Jerry said. "The problem is, the horses are tired and so am I."

"I know, but we should help others. If *my*

mother were dying, I'd want someone to help me. I'm sure it won't break the Sabbath to help Dinah, just as it wouldn't break the Sabbath to help some lost or injured animal."

"Polly, you're as good as the minister. I've had my Sunday sermon early today. Tell Dinah that I'll be ready for her at ten. Please also go to butcher Braydon and ask him if he'll lend me his gig. He never uses it on Sundays, and it would be easier on Jack."

Polly left and soon returned, saying that Braydon had readily agreed to let Jerry use the gig.

"Good," Jerry said. "Wrap me up some bread and cheese. I'll be back in the afternoon as soon as I can."

"I'll have a meat pie ready when you get back," Polly said, and she went away.

Jerry got ready while he sang "Polly's the Woman," a tune of which he was very fond.

At ten o'clock Jerry and I set out in a light, two-wheel carriage. It ran so easily that, compared to the four-wheel cab, it seemed like nothing. It was a fine May day. As soon as we were out of London, the sweet air, fresh-smelling grass, and soft country roads were as pleasant as they used to be in the old times. I soon felt quite fresh.

Dinah's family lived in a small farmhouse, up a green lane, near a meadow with some shady trees. There were two cows grazing in the meadow.

A young man said to Jerry, "Please bring your carriage into the meadow. I'll tie up your horse in the cowshed. I wish I could offer you a better stable."

Jerry said, "If your cows won't mind, there's nothing my horse would like better than an hour or two in your beautiful meadow. It'll be a rare treat for him."

"You're most welcome to leave him in the meadow," the young man said. "The best we have is at your service for your kindness to my sister. We'll be having dinner in an hour. I hope you'll join us."

"Thank you kindly," Jerry said, "but I have food with me. I'd like to walk in the meadow."

When my harness was removed, I didn't know what to do first—eat the grass, roll over on my back, lie down and rest, or gallop across the meadow out of sheer joy at being free. I did all those things.

Jerry seemed as happy as I was. He sat down by a bank under a shady tree and listened to the birds. Then he sang and read out of the small black-covered book that he was so fond of. Then he wandered around the meadow and down by a little brook, where he picked flowers and tied them with long sprays of ivy. He gave me a good meal of oats that he'd brought. The time passed too quickly. I hadn't been in a field since I left poor Ginger at Earlshall.

We came home gently. As we entered the yard, Jerry's first words were, "Well, Polly, I haven't lost my Sunday after all. The birds were singing hymns in every bush, and I joined in the service. As for Jack, he was like a colt."

When he handed Dolly the flowers, she jumped about with joy.

CHAPTER 38

Dolly and a Real Gentleman

Winter came early, very cold and wet. It snowed, sleeted, or rained almost every day for weeks, often with strong winds and sharp frosts. The horses all felt it keenly. When it's cold but dry, a couple of good thick rugs will keep us warm. But when there's a heavy rain, the rugs soon get soaked. Some of the cab drivers had a waterproof cover to throw over themselves, but others were too poor. Many drivers suffered a lot that winter. When we horses had worked half the day, we went to our dry stables and could rest, but the men had to sit on their driver's seat, sometimes staying out as late as one or two in the morning if they had to wait for a party or other event to finish.

Streets slippery with frost or snow are the worst things for horses. One mile of such travel, with a weight to pull and no firm footing, takes more out of us than four miles on a good road.

We strain every nerve and muscle to keep our balance, and the fear of falling is exhausting.

When the weather was very bad, many of the cabmen would sit in the nearby Rising Sun tavern and get someone to watch their cabs for them. But they often lost a fare that way. Also, they couldn't be in the tavern without, as Jerry said, "spending money."

Jerry never went to the Rising Sun. Now and then he went to a nearby coffee shop or bought hot coffee from an old man who came to the cab stand selling pies and tins of hot coffee. Jerry believed that alcohol made a person more susceptible to cold and that dry clothes, good food, cheerfulness, and a loving wife at home were the best things to keep a cabman warm. Polly always supplied Jerry with something to eat when he couldn't get home.

Sometimes little Dolly would peep from the street corner to see if Jerry was at the cab stand. If she saw him, she'd run off and soon return with something in a basket or tin, some hot soup or pudding that Polly had made. Dolly would bravely hurry across the street, often thronged with horses and carriages. She considered it an honor to bring Jerry his food. She was a favorite at the cab stand. There wasn't a man who wouldn't have seen her safely across the street if Jerry hadn't been able to.

One cold, windy day Dolly brought Jerry a

basin of hot soup and was standing by him as he ate it. He scarcely had begun when a gentleman walked quickly toward us, holding up his umbrella. Jerry touched his hat, gave the basin to Dolly, and was taking off my cloth when the gentleman, hurrying toward us, said, "No, no. Finish your soup, my friend. I can't spare much time, but I can wait until you've finished and set your little girl safely on the sidewalk." So saying, he seated himself in the cab.

Jerry thanked him kindly and came back to Dolly. "That's a true gentleman, Dolly. He has time and consideration for the comfort of a poor cabman and his little girl."

Jerry finished his soup, set Dolly on the sidewalk, and took his orders to drive to Clapham Rise.

Several times after that the same gentleman, Mr. Wright, took our cab. I think he was very fond of dogs and horses because whenever we took him to his own door, two dogs would bound out to greet him. Sometimes he came around and patted me. He said, "This horse has a good master, and he deserves that."

It was rare for people to notice the horse who'd been pulling them. Now and then ladies noticed, and Mr. Wright and a few other gentlemen would give me a pat and a kind word. But ninety-nine out of a hundred people would as soon pat the steam engine that powers a train.

Mr. Wright wasn't young. His shoulders stooped forward. His lips were thin and tightly shut, although he had a pleasant smile. His eyes were keen. Something in his jaw and the motion of his head indicated that he was very determined in anything he decided to do. His voice was pleasant and kind. Any horse would trust that voice.

One day Mr. Wright and another gentleman took our cab. They stopped at a shop in Restford Street. While his friend went in, Mr. Wright stood at the door. A little ahead of us on the other side of the street, a cart with two fine horses was standing in front of some wine vaults. The carter wasn't with them, and I don't know how long they'd been standing there. They seemed to think they'd waited long enough because they started to move off. Before they'd gone many paces, the carter came running out and caught them. He was furious at their having moved. He punished them brutally with whip and rein, even beating them about the head. Mr. Wright saw it all. He hurried across the street and said firmly, "Stop at once, or I'll have you arrested for cruelty."

The man, who clearly had been drinking, poured forth abusive language, but he stopped hitting the horses. Taking the reins, he got into his cart.

Mr. Wright took a notebook from his pocket and, looking at the name and address painted on the cart, wrote something down.

"What are you doing?" the carter growled as he cracked his whip and was moving on.

Mr. Wright responded only with a nod. On returning to the cab, he was joined by his companion, who said, "I would have thought that you had enough business of your own to look after without troubling yourself about other people's horses and servants."

Mr. Wright stood still for a moment. Then, throwing his head back a little, he said, "Do you know why this world is as bad as it is?"

"No," the other man said.

"I'll tell you. It's because people think about only their own business and don't bother to stand up for the oppressed or bring a wrong-doer to justice. I never witness an act of cruelty without doing what I can. Many a master has thanked me for letting him know how his horses have been treated."

"I wish there were more gentlemen like you, sir," Jerry said.

We continued our journey. As the two men got out of the cab, Mr. Wright said, "If we see cruelty or some other wrong that we have the power to stop and we do nothing, we share in the guilt."

CHAPTER 39

Seedy Sam

I was very well-off for a cab horse. My driver was my owner; it was in his interest to treat me well and not overwork me, even if he hadn't been such a good man.

But many horses belonged to owners, such as Nicholas Skinner, who rented them out to cab drivers for a daily fee. Because the horses didn't belong to the drivers, the drivers thought only of how to make the most money out of them. Some of these horses were dreadfully abused. The men at the cab stand often talked about this.

Mr. Grant, who was kindhearted and fond of horses, sometimes spoke up if a horse looked wretched. One day a shabby, miserable-looking driver called Seedy Sam brought in an exhausted horse. Mr. Grant said, "Your horse looks so weak, I should call the police."

Sam flung his tattered rug over the horse,

turned around to Mr. Grant, and said angrily, "If anyone should be arrested, it's the men who charge us cabmen so much or the people who fix the cab fares so low. If a man has to pay eighteen shillings a day to use a cab and two horses, as many of us do, and has to make that up before he earns a penny for himself, it's more than hard work. We have to get nine shillings out of each horse before we begin to earn anything. If the horses don't work, we starve. My children and I have known hunger. I have six children. Only one of them earns anything. I'm at the cab stand sixteen hours a day. I haven't had a Sunday off in three months. If I don't work hard, I don't know who does! I need a warm coat and a rain-coat, but with so many to feed, how can I get them? A week ago I had to pawn my clock to pay Skinner. I'll never see it again."

Some of the other drivers stood around nodding and saying that he was right.

Sam went on. "Those of you who have your own horses and cabs, or who drive for good masters, have a chance of getting on and doing all right. I don't. Within the four-mile radius, we can't charge more than sixpence a mile after the first mile. This morning I had to go six miles and got only three shillings. I couldn't get a return fare, so I came all the way back without getting paid for that time and travel. That's twelve miles for the horse and three shillings for me. After that I had a three-mile fare. There were enough boxes and bags to bring in many twopence if they'd been put outside. But you know what people do. They crammed everything they could inside on the front seat, and three heavy boxes went on top. That was sixpence, and the fare was one and sixpence. Then I got a return fare of a shilling. That makes eighteen miles for the horse and six shillings for me. That horse still has to earn three shillings and the afternoon horse has to earn nine shillings before I make a penny. It isn't always that bad, but it often is. It's a mockery to tell a man that he mustn't overwork his horse. When horses are exhausted, only the whip will keep their legs going. You can't help yourself. You have to put your wife and children before the horse. The masters must look to the horses; we can't. I don't abuse my horse out of choice. I never have a day's rest or a quiet hour with my wife and children. I often feel like an old man, although I'm only forty-five. You know how quick some of the gentry are to suspect us of cheating and overcharging. They look at us as if we were pickpockets. I wish some of them had to sit on a driver's seat sixteen hours a day in all kinds of weather and make a living from it. They wouldn't be so unwilling to give us a sixpence tip or so eager to cram all their luggage inside. Some of them give us a generous tip now and then, and that keeps us alive. But you can't depend on that."

The men who stood around approved of Sam's speech. One of them said, "It's desperate hard. It's no wonder a man sometimes does wrong. And if he drinks too much, who can blame him?"

Jerry took no part in this conversation, but I'd never seen him look so sad.

Mr. Grant had stood with his hands in his pockets. Now he took his handkerchief out of his hat and wiped his forehead. "You're right, Sam. I won't threaten you with the police anymore. The look in that horse's eyes really got to me. It's a hard time for men and a hard time for horses. Still, you might at least tell the poor horse that you're sorry to press him that way. Sometimes a kind word is all we can give them, poor creatures, and I think they understand."

A few mornings later a new man came to the stand with Sam's cab.

"Where's Sam?" someone asked.

"He's bedridden," the newcomer said. "He took ill last night and barely could crawl home. His wife sent a boy this morning to say that he has a high fever and can't get out, so I'm here instead."

The next morning the same man came again.

"How's Sam?" Mr. Grant asked.

"He died," the man said.

"What?"

"He died at four o'clock this morning. Yesterday he raved all day—about Skinner and about having no Sundays to rest. His last words were, 'I never had a Sunday's rest.'"

For a while no one spoke.

CHAPTER 40

Poor Ginger

One day, while our cab and many others were waiting outside a park where music was playing, a shabby old cab drove up beside ours. The horse was an old, worn-out, and emaciated chestnut. Her knees knuckled over, and her forelegs were unsteady. I had been eating some hay. The wind rolled a small piece of it her way. The poor creature put out her long, thin neck; ate the piece of hay; then turned and looked around for more. There was a hopeless look in her dull eyes. As I was thinking, "Where have I seen that horse before?" she looked directly at me and exclaimed, "Black Beauty, is that you?"

It was Ginger! The beautifully arched, glossy neck now was straight and limp. The clean, straight legs and delicate fetlocks now were swollen. Her joints were deformed from hard work. Her face, once so full of spirit and life, was full of suffering. Her sides heaved, and she frequently coughed.

Our drivers were standing together a little way off. I sidled up to Ginger, so that we could talk. Her tale was a sad one. After a year's rest at Earlshall, she was considered fit for work and sold to a gentleman. For a short time she got on well. However, after a longer gallop than usual, the old strain returned. After being rested and doctored, she was sold again. She changed hands several times, always sinking lower.

"Finally," she said, "I was bought by a man named Skinner. He owns a number of cabs and horses and rents them out. You look well-off, and I'm glad. I can't even tell you what my life has been like. When Skinner discovered my weakness, he said I wasn't worth what he'd paid for me. He put me with one of the low cabs to be used up. The man who rents me pays Skinner every day, so he has to get his money's worth out of me. He whips me and works me with no thought of what I suffer. I'm forced to work the entire week. I never rest, not even on Sundays."

I said, "You used to stand up for yourself if you were abused."

"It's no use," she said. "Humans have all the power. If they're insensitive and cruel, there's nothing we can do except bear it, bear it on and on until the end. I wish the end would come. I wish I were dead. I've seen dead horses. I'm sure they don't suffer anymore. I hope

I'll drop dead while I'm working and not be sent to the slaughterer."

I was greatly troubled. I put my nose up to Ginger's, but I couldn't say anything to comfort her.

She said, "You're the only friend I've ever had."

Her driver came up and, with a tug at her mouth, backed her out of the line and drove off, leaving me very sad.

A short time later a cart with a dead horse in it passed our cab stand. The horse's head hung out the back of the cart. The lifeless tongue dripped blood. The eyes were sunken. It was a chestnut horse with a long, thin neck. I saw a white streak down the forehead. Ginger! I grieved but was glad that her suffering was over.

CHAPTER 41

The Butcher

I saw much suffering among London's horses. A little common sense would have prevented a lot of it. We horses don't mind hard work if we're treated well. I'm sure that many horses driven by poor people are happier than I was when I pulled Lady Helen's carriage, with my silver-mounted harness.

It often saddened me to see how the little ponies were abused. They strained under heavy loads or staggered under blows from low, cruel boys. Once I saw a little gray pony with a thick mane and a pretty head. He was so much like Merrylegs that I almost neighed to him. He was doing his best to pull a heavy cart. A strong, rough boy was cutting him on the belly with his whip and jerking cruelly at his little mouth.

Butchers' horses often are made to go at great speed. One day when Jerry and I were waiting next to a butcher's shop, a butcher's cart came dashing up. The pony was hot and exhausted. His head hung down, his sides heaved, and his legs trembled.

The boy jumped out of the cart and was getting the basket when the butcher came out of the shop. After looking at the pony, the butcher turned angrily to the boy. "How many times have I told you not to drive this way? You ruined the last horse and broke his wind. You aren't going to ruin this horse, too. If you weren't my son, I'd fire you on the spot. It's a disgrace to have a horse brought to the shop in this condition. The police could arrest you for such driving. If they do, don't expect me to bail you out."

The boy sullenly responded, "It isn't my fault. You always say, 'Be quick!' At one house the cook wanted a leg of mutton for an early dinner, and I had to bring it within fifteen minutes. At another house the cook had forgotten to order the beef; I had to fetch it immediately, or the mistress would scold. At another house the housekeeper said they had company coming unexpectedly and must have some chops sent up at once. The lady at Number 4 in the Crescent never orders her dinner until the meat comes in for lunch. It's nothing but hurry, hurry all the time. If the gentry would decide what they want and order their meat the day before, it wouldn't be this way!"

"I wish to goodness they would," the butcher said. "It would save me a lot of trouble, and I could fill orders better if I knew beforehand. But who ever considers a butcher's convenience or a butcher's horse? Take the pony in, and look to him well. Mind, he's not to go out again today. If anything else is wanted, you'll have to carry it yourself in the basket."

The boy went in, and the pony was led away.

Not all boys are cruel. Some are extremely fond of their ponies or donkeys, who work as willingly and cheerfully for their young drivers as I worked for Jerry. A friend's hand and voice can make hard work seem easy.

There was a young boy who would come down our street selling potatoes and green vegetables. He had an old pony, not very handsome but the liveliest and most cheerful little thing I ever saw. It was a treat to see how fond those two were of each other. The pony would follow his master like a dog. When the boy got into his cart, the pony would trot off without a whip or a word and rattle down the street as merrily as if he'd come out of the queen's stables. Jerry liked the boy and called him Prince Charlie because, Jerry said, he'd make a king of drivers some day.

There was an old man, too, who would come down our street with a little coal cart. He looked rough and black. He and his old horse would plod along the street together, like two good partners who understood each other. Of his own accord the horse would stop at the doors of people who bought coal. He'd keep one ear bent toward his master. Polly bought coal from this man. Jerry said it was a comfort to think how happy an old horse could be in a poor place.

CHAPTER 42

Election Day

As we entered the yard one afternoon, Polly came out. "Jerry, Mr. Bestford has been here asking for your vote. He wants to hire your cab for election day. He'll call for an answer."

"Say that my cab will be otherwise engaged. I don't want to make Jack and Captain race around to bars to collect half-drunk men for voting. I won't do it."

On election day there was no lack of work for Jerry and me. First came a stout, puffy gentleman with a carpet bag. He wanted to go to Bishopsgate Station. Then we were called by a group who wanted to go to Regent's Park. Next we were wanted in a side street where a timid, anxious old lady was waiting to be taken to the bank. We took her there and then waited to take her back. Just as we set her down, a red-faced gentleman came running up, out of breath, with a handful of papers. Before Jerry could get down, he had opened the door, popped in, and called out, "Bow Street Police Station! Quick!" So off we went with him. When we came back after another turn, there was no other cab at the stand.

Jerry gave me my nose bag of food. "On days like this, we have to eat when we can," he said. "So munch away, Jack. Make the best of your time, old boy." The food was crushed oats wetted with a little bran—a treat any day and very refreshing then. Jerry was so thoughtful and kind. What horse wouldn't do their best for such a master?

Jerry took out one of Polly's meat pies and, standing near me, began to eat it. The streets were full, and the cabs were dashing through the crowd as if life and limb were of no consequence.

We saw one woman and one man knocked down that day. The horses were having a bad time, but the voters inside the cabs thought nothing of that. Many of them were half-drunk.

Jerry and I hadn't eaten many mouthfuls when a poor young woman, carrying a child, came along the street. She looked here and there and seemed bewildered. She made her way up to Jerry and asked if he could tell her the way to St. Thomas's Hospital and how far it was. She'd come from the countryside that morning in a market cart. She was unfamiliar with London. Her little boy was crying feebly. "Poor little fellow!" she said. "He's in pain. He's four years old but can't walk. The doctor said that if I could get him into the hospital, he might get well. Pray, sir, how far is it and which way?"

"Why, Mrs., you can't walk through these crowds. It's three miles away, and that child is heavy."

"Yes, he is, but I'm strong. I'll manage. Please tell me the way."

"You might be knocked down and the child run over," Jerry said. "Get into my cab, and I'll drive you to the hospital. It's about to rain."

"Thank you, but I have only enough money for my return trip."

"I have children I dearly love. I know a parent's feelings. Get into the cab. I'll take you there for nothing. I'd be ashamed if I didn't."

"Heaven bless you!" the woman said, and she burst into tears.

"Cheer up, my dear. You'll be there soon. Let me help you inside."

As Jerry went to open the door, two men ran up, calling out, "Cab!"

"Engaged," Jerry said.

Pushing past the woman, one of the men sprang into the cab, followed by the other.

Jerry looked as stern as a policeman. "This cab is already engaged, gentlemen, by that lady."

"Lady?" one of them sneered. "She can wait. Our business is important. Besides, we were in first, so the cab is rightly ours."

Jerry shut the door on them. "All right, gentlemen, stay there as long as you like." Turning his back on them, he walked up to the young woman, who was standing near me. "They'll be gone soon," he said, laughing. "Don't worry, my dear."

And so they were. When they understood that Jerry had no intention of taking them anywhere, they got out, calling him all sorts of bad names and blustering about taking down the number of his cab and having the police give him a summons.

We soon were on our way to the hospital, going as much as possible through side streets. Jerry rang the hospital's doorbell and helped the young woman out of the cab.

"Thank you a thousand times," she said. "I never could have gotten here alone."

"You're most welcome. I hope your child will be well soon."

Jerry watched her go in. Then he patted my neck, as he always did when something pleased him. The rain was heavy now.

Just as we were leaving the hospital, the door opened and the porter called out, "Cab!"

We stopped, and a lady came down the steps. Jerry knew her at once. She put back her veil and said, "Jeremiah! I'm very glad to find you here. You're just the friend I need. It's very difficult to get a cab in this part of London today."

"Proud to serve you, ma'am. I'm glad I

happened to be here. Where may I take you?"

"To Paddington Station, please. If we make good time, you can tell me all about Polly and the children."

We got to the station in good time. Standing under shelter, the lady talked to Jerry for a while. I found out that she'd been Polly's employer. After many inquiries about Polly, the lady asked, "Does cab work suit you in the winter? Polly was rather anxious about you last year."

"Yes, ma'am. I had a bad cough that lasted into the warm weather. When I'm kept out late, she worries. You see, ma'am, it's all hours and all kinds of weather, and that does tax a man's constitution. But I'm getting on pretty well. I'd feel lost if I didn't have horses to look after. I was brought up to it. I don't think I'd do anything else as well."

"Well, Jeremiah," she said, "it would be a great pity if you damaged your health in this work. Many places need good drivers or grooms. If you ever decide to give up cab work, let me know."

She conveyed kind messages to Polly and said, "Here's five shillings each for the two children. Polly will know how to spend it."

Jerry thanked her and seemed very pleased. We turned out of the station.

When we finally reached home, I was very tired.

CHAPTER 43

Old Captain and His Successor

Jerry and Captain were returning from a railway station when a brewer's empty cart approached, drawn by two powerful horses. The driver lashed his horses with his heavy whip. The cart was light, and the horses started off at a furious pace. The man had no control over them, and the street was full of traffic. One young girl was knocked down and run over.

The next moment the horses dashed up against Jerry's cab. Both of the wheels were torn off, and the cab was overturned. Captain was dragged down. The shafts splintered, and one of them ran into his side. Jerry was thrown, but he was only bruised. Poor Captain—my great and noble friend—was seriously injured. Jerry led him home gently. It was sad to see the blood soaking into his white coat and dropping from his side and shoulder. The horse doctor and

Jerry did the best they could to ease Captain's pain and make him comfortable.

The cart driver was found to have been drunk. He was fined. The brewer had to pay damages to Jerry, but no one paid damages to poor Captain.

The cab had to be mended, so I didn't go out for several days. The first time we went to the cab stand after the accident, Mr. Grant asked how Captain was.

"He'll never recover," Jerry said, "at least, not enough to be a cab horse. The horse doctor said so this morning. He said that Captain might be able to pull a cart. I'm very upset. Pull a cart! I've seen how cart horses are treated in London. I wish all the drunkards could be put in a lunatic asylum instead of being allowed to hurt people and horses. If they'd break their own bones, that would be fine with me, but the innocent suffer. They talk of compensation for accidents caused by drunkards. There's no compensation for the trouble, distress, and lost time, not to mention a good horse who's an old friend."

At first Captain seemed to do well, but he was very old. Only his wonderful constitution and Jerry's care had kept him at cab work this long. Now he broke down. The horse doctor said he might heal enough to sell for a few pounds.

Jerry said, "No. I won't sell a good old servant into hard work and misery. The kindest thing I can do for the fine old fellow is put a bullet through his head. Then he won't suffer anymore."

The day after this was decided, Harry took me to the blacksmith for some new shoes. When I returned, Captain was gone. The family and I grieved.

Jerry had to look for another horse. He soon heard about one through an acquaintance who was under-groom in a nobleman's stables. He was a valuable young horse, but he'd run away, smashed into another carriage, flung his lordship out, and so cut and blemished himself that he no longer was fit for a gentleman's stables. The coachman had orders to look around and sell him as well as he could.

"I like high spirits," Jerry said, "if a horse isn't vicious or hard-mouthed."

"There's no vice in him," the man said. "His mouth is tender. I think that caused the accident. You see, the weather was bad, and he hadn't had enough exercise. So when he did go out, he was as full of spring as a balloon. The coachman had him harnessed in as tight and strong as he could, with the martingale, the checkrein, a very sharp curb, and the reins put in at the bottom bar. I think that made the horse crazy, being tender in the mouth and so full of spirit."

"That's likely. I'll come see him," Jerry said.

The next day Hotspur—that was his name—came home. He was a fine brown horse only five years old. He was as tall as Captain, with a very handsome head. I gave him a friendly greeting but didn't ask him any questions.

The first night Hotspur was very restless. He was tethered to a large ring on a block by the manger. Instead of lying down, he kept jerking the tether up and down within the ring and knocking the block about against the manger. This prevented me from sleeping.

However, the next day, after five or six hours in the cab, Hotspur came in quiet and sensible. Jerry patted and talked to him a lot, and they soon understood each other. Jerry said that with an easy bit and plenty of work, Hotspur would be as gentle as a lamb. He said that his lordship had lost a hundred-guinea favorite, but *he* had gained a good, strong horse.

Hotspur thought it a great come-down to be a cab horse and was disgusted at having to stand in the cab line. But he confessed to me at the end of the week that an easy mouth and a free head made up for a lot, and, after all, the work wasn't as degrading as having one's head and tail fastened to each other at the saddle.

Hotspur settled in well, and Jerry liked him very much.

CHAPTER 44

Jerry's New Year

For many people Christmas and New Year's are merry times, but for cabmen and their horses they're times of hard work. There are so many parties, balls, and other celebrations that the work is hard and often late. Sometimes driver and horse have to wait hours, shivering, in the rain or frost while the merry people inside are dancing. I wonder if the beautiful ladies and handsome gentlemen ever think of the weary cabmen waiting on their driver's seat and their patient horses standing until their legs are stiff with cold.

I did most of the evening work because I was accustomed to standing and Jerry was afraid that Hotspur might take cold. We had a lot of late work during Christmas week. Jerry's cough was bad. However late we were, Polly sat up for him and came out with a lantern to meet him, looking anxious and troubled.

On New Year's Eve we had to take two gentlemen to a house in one of the West End squares. We set them down at nine o'clock and were told to come back at eleven. "Because it's a card party," one said, "you might have to wait a few minutes, but don't be late."

Jerry always was punctual, so we were at the door when the clock struck eleven. The clock chimed the quarters—one, then two, then three—and then struck midnight, but the door didn't open.

Sharp, driving sleet came from every direction. It was very cold, and there was no shelter. Jerry got off his driver's seat and came and pulled one of my cloths a little more over my neck. Then he walked up and down, stamping his feet. He began to beat his arms, but that got him coughing. He opened the cab door and sat at the bottom with his feet on the pavement, so that he was somewhat sheltered. Still the clock chimed the quarters, and no one came.

At half-past midnight Jerry rang the bell and asked the servant, "Will I be wanted tonight?"

"Oh yes, you'll be wanted," the man said. "You mustn't go. It'll be over soon."

Jerry sat down again.

At 1:15 the door opened, and the two gentlemen came out. Without a word they got into the cab and told Jerry where to drive. My legs were so numb with cold that I thought I'd stumble.

When the men got out, they didn't apologize for keeping us waiting so long. They were angry when Jerry charged them for the two hours and a quarter of waiting. But that was only fair, and it was hard earned.

When we finally got home, Jerry hardly could speak, and his cough was dreadful. Polly opened the door and held the lantern for him. "Can I do something?" she asked.

"Get Jack something warm. Then boil me some gruel." This was said in a hoarse whisper. Jerry hardly could catch his breath.

Even so, he rubbed me down as usual and went up into the hayloft for an extra bundle of straw for my bed. Polly brought me a warm mash that made me comfortable. Then they locked the door.

It was late the next morning before anyone came, and then it was only Harry. He cleaned and fed Hotspur and me and swept out our stalls. Then he put straw down as if it were Sunday. He was very quiet. He didn't whistle or sing.

At noon Harry came again and gave us our food and water. This time Dolly came with him. She was crying. I could tell from what they said that Jerry was dangerously ill. The doctor had said so.

Two days passed. Hotspur and I saw only Harry and sometimes Dolly. I think that Dolly came for company because Polly always was with Jerry, and he had to be kept very quiet.

On the third day, there was a tap at the stable door while Harry was in the stable. Mr. Grant came in. "I didn't want to go to the house, my boy," he said, "but I'd like to know how your father is."

"He's very bad," Harry said. "The doctor said he has bronchitis."

Mr. Grant shook his head. "Two men died of that last week, but we must keep our hopes up."

"Yes," Harry said quickly. "The doctor said that Father has a better chance than most men because he doesn't drink. He said that yesterday the fever was so high that if Father had been a drinking man, it would have burned him up like a piece of paper. I believe the doctor thinks he'll recover."

"If there's any rule that good men get over these things, then your father will. He's the best man I know. I'll look in early tomorrow."

Early next morning Mr. Grant came again. "Well?" he asked.

"Father is better," Harry said. "Mother thinks he'll get well."

"Thank God!" Mr. Grant said. "Keep him warm, and keep his mind easy. That brings me to the horses. Jack will be all the better for a week or two of rest in a warm stable, and you can easily take him for a turn up and down the street to stretch his legs. But this young one—if he doesn't work, he'll get tense."

"Hotspur already *is* tense," Harry said. "I've given him less corn, but he's so high-spirited that I don't know what to do with him."

"Exactly," Mr. Grant said. "Tell your mother that if she's agreeable, I'll come for Hotspur every day and take him for a good spell of work. I'll bring your mother half of whatever he earns. That'll help pay for the horses' food. I'll come back at noon for your mother's decision." He left without waiting for Harry's thanks.

At noon Mr. Grant went and saw Polly. Then Harry and Mr. Grant came to the stable, harnessed Hotspur, and took him out.

For a week or more Mr. Grant came for Hotspur. When Harry thanked him or said anything about his kindness, he laughed it off, saying it was good for him because his horses needed a rest, which they wouldn't have had otherwise.

Jerry steadily recovered, but the doctor said that he shouldn't ever return to cab work.

One afternoon Hotspur was brought in very wet and dirty. "The streets are nothing but slush," Mr. Grant said. "Get him clean and dry, my boy."

"Yes, Mr. Grant," Harry said. "I won't leave him until he is. I've been trained by my father."

"I wish all boys were trained like you," Mr. Grant said.

While Harry was sponging the mud off Hotspur's body and legs, Dolly came in, looking excited. "Who lives at Fairstowe, Harry? Mother has received a letter from Fairstowe. She seemed very glad and ran up to Father with it."

"That's Mrs. Fowler's place—mother's former employer, the lady who sent you and me five shillings each last summer."

"Oh, Mrs. Fowler! I wonder what she's writing to Mother about."

"Mother wrote to her last week," Harry said. "Mrs. Fowler told Father that if he ever gave up cab work, he should let her know. I wonder what she said. Run in and see, Dolly."

Harry scrubbed away at Hotspur with a huish, huish, like any old hostler.

In a few minutes Dolly came dancing into the stable. "Oh Harry, there never was anything so wonderful! Mrs. Fowler says we are all to go and live near her. There's an empty cottage that will suit us perfectly, with a garden, a henhouse, apple trees, and everything! Her coachman is leaving in the spring. She wants Father to take his place. There are good families there. You'll be able to get a job in a garden or stable or as a page boy. And there's a good school for me. Mother is laughing and crying with joy, and Father looks so happy!"

"That's wonderful," Harry said. "Just the right thing. It'll suit Father and Mother. I don't intend to be a page boy, with tight clothes and rows of buttons. I'll be a groom or gardener."

It was quickly settled: as soon as Jerry was well enough, the family would move to the country; the cab, Hotspur, and I would be sold. This was sad news for me. I wasn't young anymore and couldn't expect any improvement in my condition. Since I'd left Birtwick Park, I'd never been as happy as with Jerry. But three years of cab work, even under the best conditions, sap a horse's strength. I knew I wasn't the horse that I'd been before.

Mr. Grant said that he'd take Hotspur. There were men at the cab stand who would have bought me, but Jerry said I shouldn't return to cab work with just anyone.

The day came for going away. Jerry hadn't been allowed to go out yet. I hadn't seen him since New Year's Eve. Polly and the children came to bid me goodbye.

"Poor old Jack! Dear old Jack! I wish we could take you with us," Polly said. Laying her hand on my mane, she put her face against my neck and kissed me. Dolly was crying and kissed me, too. Harry stroked me a lot but didn't say anything. He seemed very sad.

I was led away to my new place.

CHAPTER 45

Jakes and the Lady

I was sold to a corn dealer and baker whom Jerry knew. Jerry thought that I'd have good food and fair work with him. I did get good food. And I don't think I would have been overworked if my master always had been on the premises, but there was a foreman who was always hurrying everyone. Often when I already had a full load, he'd order something else to be added. My carter, Jakes, often said the load was more than I should take, but the foreman always overruled him. "There's no use going twice when once will do," the foreman would say.

Like the other carters, Jakes used a checkrein, which prevented me from pulling easily. By the time I'd been at the corn dealer's several months, the work was taking quite a toll on my strength.

One day I was loaded more heavily than usual. Part of the road was steeply uphill. I used all my strength but couldn't move steadily upward. I continually had to stop. This displeased Jakes, who whipped me severely. "Get on, you lazy fellow," he said, "or I'll make you." Again I tried to pull the heavy load. I struggled on for a few yards. Again the great whip came down. The pain was sharp, but my mind hurt as much as my sides. To be abused when I was doing my best took the heart out of me.

Jakes was cruelly flogging me for a third time when a lady quickly stepped up to him and said, "Don't whip your good horse anymore. He's doing all he can. The road is very steep. I'm sure he's doing his best."

"If doing his best won't get this load up, he has to do more than his best," Jakes said.

"It's a heavy load," she said.

"Yes, too heavy, but that's not my fault. The foreman came just as we were starting and added three hundred more pounds." Jakes raised the whip again.

"Stop! I can help if you'll let me."

Jakes laughed skeptically.

"You aren't giving him a fair chance. He can't use all of his strength with his head held back by that checkrein. If you take it off, he'll do better."

"Very well," Jakes said with a short laugh. "How far down do you want it?"

"Take it off."

The rein was removed. In a moment I put my head down to my very knees. What a comfort that was! Then I tossed my head up and down several times to get the aching stiffness out of my neck.

"Poor fellow! That's what you wanted," the lady said, patting and stroking me with her gentle hand. "Now if you'll speak kindly to him and lead him on, I believe he'll be able to do better."

Jakes took the rein. "Come on, Blackie." I put my head down and threw my whole weight against the collar. I spared no strength. The load moved on. I pulled it steadily up the hill and then stopped for breath.

The lady had walked along the footpath and now came across into the road. She stroked and patted my neck as I hadn't been patted for a long time. "You see, he was quite willing when you gave him the chance. I'm sure he's a fine-tempered creature. I dare say he's known better days."

Jakes started to put the checkrein back on.

"Don't put that on again," the lady said.

"Well, ma'am, I can't deny that having his head free helped him up the hill. I'll remember that the next time. But if he went without a checkrein, I'd be the laughingstock of all the carters. It's the fashion, you see."

"Isn't it better to start a good fashion than to follow a bad one? Many gentlemen don't use checkreins. Our carriage horses haven't worn them for fifteen years. They work with much less fatigue than those who have them. Besides, we have no right to distress any creature. Animals can't tell us how they feel, but that doesn't mean that they suffer any less. You'll find my plan far better than a whip. Good day." After another soft pat on my neck, she left.

Jakes let my rein out several holes. From then on, whenever I had to go uphill, he left my head free. But the heavy loads continued. Good food and fair rest couldn't make up for continual heavy loading. I was getting so weak that a younger horse was bought to replace me.

At this time I also suffered from poor lighting in my stable, which had only one small window at the end. The stalls were almost dark. Besides depressing me, this strained my eyes. Whenever I was suddenly brought out of the darkness into the glare of daylight, my eyes hurt. Several times I stumbled over the threshold and scarcely could see where I was going. I think that if I'd stayed at the corn dealer's much longer, I would have become weak-sighted. I escaped permanent damage to my eyesight because I was sold again.

CHAPTER 46

Hard Times

My new master was Nicholas Skinner, the man poor Seedy Sam had driven for and who had owned Ginger at the wretched end of her life. Skinner had black eyes and a hooked nose. His mouth was as full of teeth as a bulldog's. His voice was as harsh as the grinding of cart wheels over gravel.

For the first time, I knew just how miserable a cab horse's life can be. Skinner had a low set of cabs and a low set of drivers. He was hard on the men, who were hard on the horses. We had no Sunday rest, and it was in the heat of summer.

Sometimes on Sunday morning a group of men would hire the cab for the day—four of them inside and another with the driver. I had to take them ten or fifteen miles out into the countryside and back. None of them ever would get down to walk up a hill, however steep it was and however hot the weather, except when the driver was afraid I wouldn't be able to climb the hill.

Sometimes I was so feverish and worn that I hardly could eat. I longed for the bran mash that Jerry had given me on Saturday nights in hot weather. That had cooled me down and made me comfortable.

Jerry had given me two nights and a whole day of unbroken rest every week. On Monday morning I'd be as fresh as a young horse. Here there was no rest. And my driver was as hard as his master. His whip was so sharp that it sometimes drew blood. He'd even whip me on my belly and flip the lash at my head. However much I suffered, I did my best and never hung back because, as poor Ginger had said, humans have all the power. It was useless to resist. My life was so wretched that, like Ginger, I wanted to die.

One day my wish nearly came true. I went to the cab stand at eight in the morning. I'd already done a good deal of work when we had to take a passenger to the railway. A long train was expected in, so my driver pulled up in the hope of getting a return fare. Because the train was crowded, all of the cabs soon were engaged.

My cab took a family of four with lots of luggage: a loud father, his wife, and their little boy and girl. The mother and boy got into the cab.

While the father arranged the luggage, the little girl came and looked at me. "Papa," she said, "I'm sure this poor horse can't take us and all our luggage so far. He's very weak and worn.

Look at him."

"Oh, he's all right, Miss," my driver said. "He's strong enough."

The porter, who was pulling some heavy boxes, suggested to the father that, since there was so much luggage, he should consider hiring a second cab.

"Can your horse do it or not?" the father asked the cabman.

"Yes, he can do it, sir. Send up the boxes, porter. He could take more than that." My driver helped haul up a box so heavy that I could feel the cab's springs press down.

"Papa, please hire a second cab," the young girl begged. "I'm sure we're wrong. I'm sure it's cruel."

"Nonsense, Grace. Get in, and stop making such a fuss. The man knows his own business."

The gentle girl obeyed.

Box after box was dragged up and lodged on top of the cab or set by the driver's side. Finally everything was ready. With his usual jerk at the rein and slash of the whip, the driver drove out of the station.

The load was very heavy. I hadn't had any food or rest since morning, but I did my best, as always, in spite of the cruelty and injustice. I got along fairly well until we came to Ludgate Hill. There the heavy load and my exhaustion overpowered me. I struggled to continue, goaded by constant jerks of the rein and use of the whip.

Suddenly my feet slipped from under me. I fell heavily to the ground, onto my side. The suddenness and force with which I fell knocked the breath out of my body. I lay perfectly still. I couldn't move. I thought I was going to die.

I heard confusion around me—loud, angry voices and the removal of luggage—but it was like a dream. I heard the little girl say, "Oh, that poor horse! It's all our fault." Someone came and loosened the throat strap of my bridle and undid the traces that kept the collar so tight. Someone said, "I think he's dead." Then I heard a policeman giving orders.

I didn't open my eyes. I could only draw a gasping breath now and then. Cold water was thrown over my head, and cordial was poured into my mouth. I was covered with something. I don't know how long I lay there, but I found my life coming back. A kind-voiced man patted me and encouraged me to rise.

After I was given some more cordial, and after I made one or two attempts to rise, I staggered to my feet and was gently led to some nearby stables. I was put into a well-littered stall and brought some warm gruel, which I drank thankfully.

In the evening I was sufficiently recovered to be led back to Skinner's stables, where I think the men did the best for me that they could.

In the morning Skinner came with a horse

doctor to look at me. The horse doctor examined me closely and said, "This is a case of overwork. If you could give him a rest for six months, he'd be able to work again. But now he doesn't have an ounce of strength left."

"Then, he can go to the dogs," Skinner said. "I don't have any meadows in which to nurse sick horses. He might get well or not. That sort of gamble doesn't suit my business. My approach is to work horses as long as they'll go, then sell them for whatever they'll fetch at the slaughterer's or elsewhere."

"His wind isn't broken," the horse doctor said. "A horse sale is coming up in about ten days. If you rest him and feed him, he might pick up. You might get more than his skin is worth."

Somewhat unwillingly, I think, Skinner followed the horse doctor's advice. He ordered that I should be well-fed and well cared for.

The stableman carried out the orders much more gladly than they were given. Ten days of absolute rest and plenty of good oats, hay, and bran mashes with boiled linseed considerably improved my condition. The linseed mashes were delicious. I decided that, after all, it might be better to live than to die.

Twelve days after my collapse, I was taken to the sale, a few miles from London. I thought that any change in my life would be an improvement, so I held my head up and hoped for the best.

CHAPTER 47

Farmer Thoroughgood and His Grandson Willie

At the sale I found myself in the company of many old, broken-down horses. Some were lame; some were broken-winded. Some should have been shot to end their suffering.

Among the buyers were many poor old men trying to get a horse, for a few pounds, who might drag a cart of wood or coal. There were poor men trying to sell worn-out horses for two or three pounds rather than have the greater loss of killing them.

Some of the men looked as if poverty and hard times had hardened them all over. Others were poor and shabby but kind, with voices I could trust; I willingly would have used the last of my strength to serve them. One tottering old man took a great liking to me and I to him, but I wasn't strong enough.

I noticed a man in a broad-rimmed hat who looked like a gentleman farmer, with a young boy at his side. He had a kind, ruddy face and a broad back and round shoulders. When he came up to my companions and me, he stood still and gave us a pitying look. His eyes rested on me. I still had a handsome mane and tail. I pricked my ears and looked at him.

"There's a horse, Willie, who has known better days."

"Poor old fellow," the boy said. "Do you think he ever was a carriage horse, Grandpa?"

"Yes," the farmer said, coming closer. "He might have been anything when he was young. Look at his nostrils and ears, the shape of his neck and shoulder. There's considerable breeding in that horse." He gave me a kind pat on the neck.

In response to his kindness, I put out my nose.

The boy stroked my face. "Poor old fellow! Look how well he understands kindness, Grandpa. Couldn't you buy him and make him young again, as you did with Ladybird?"

"My dear boy, I can't make old horses young. Ladybird wasn't that old. She was run down because she'd been abused."

"Well, Grandpa, I don't think this one is that old either. Look at his mane and tail. Look into his mouth, and then you'll know. He's very thin, but his eyes aren't sunken as with some old horses."

The old gentleman laughed. "Bless you! You're as horsy as your old grandfather."

"Do look at his mouth, Grandpa, and ask the price. I'm sure he'd grow young in our meadows."

The man who had brought me for sale now said, "The young gentleman's a knowing one, sir. This horse has been overworked in the cabs. He's not old. The horse doctor said that six months of rest would set him right. His wind isn't broken. I've tended him for ten days. I've never met a more pleasant or grateful animal. It would be worth your while to give a five-pound note for him and give him a chance. I believe he'd be worth twenty pounds by the spring."

The old gentleman laughed.

The little boy looked up eagerly. "Grandpa, didn't you say that the colt sold for five pounds more than you expected? Use that five pounds to buy this one!"

The farmer slowly felt my legs, which were very swollen and strained. Then he looked at my mouth. "Thirteen or fourteen years old, I think. Please trot him out."

I arched my poor thin neck, raised my tail a little, and threw out my legs, which were very stiff, as well as I could.

"What's the lowest price you'll take for him?" the farmer asked as I came back.

"Five pounds, sir. I was instructed to go no lower."

"It's a gamble," the old gentleman said, shaking his head. But he slowly pulled out his purse. "Do you have any more business here?" he asked, counting the sovereigns into his hand.

"No, sir. If you like, I can take him to the inn for you."

"Please do that. I'm going there now."

They walked forward, and I was led behind. The boy hardly could control his delight, and the old gentleman clearly enjoyed his grandson's pleasure.

I had a good meal at the inn. Then I was gently ridden home by a servant of my new master and turned into a large meadow with a shed in one corner.

My new master, Mr. Thoroughgood, gave orders that I should have hay and oats every morning and night and the run of the meadow during the day. "You must oversee his care, Willie," he said. "I entrust him to you."

Willie was proud of his charge and undertook it in all seriousness. He visited me every day, sometimes picking me out from among the other horses and giving me a bit of carrot or some other treat, sometimes standing by me while I ate my oats. He always came with kind words and caresses. I grew very fond of him. He called me Old Crony because I'd come to him

idsome is as handsome does," Mr.
hgood responded. "You're taking him
I'm sure you'll do well with him. If he
afe as any horse you ever drove, send
."

led to my new home, placed in a com-
stable, fed, and left to myself.

next day, the groom was cleaning my
n he said to himself, "That's just like
that Black Beauty had. He's much the
ght, too. I wonder where Black Beauty
The groom began to look me over
, talking to himself. "White star on his
.. One white foot." Looking at the mid-
y back, he exclaimed, "There's the little
white hair! It's Black Beauty! Beauty,
now me—Joe Green, who almost killed
verjoyed, he patted me and patted me.
now was a fine, grown-up fellow with
iskers and a man's voice. I put my nose
n, to let him know that we were friends.
aw a man so pleased.

ve you on trial, indeed!" Joe said. "They
e thrilled to have you! I'd like to know
undrel hurt your knees, my old Beauty.
st have been abused. Well, that's over
ish John Manly were here to see you."

he afternoon I was hitched to a small,
rriage and brought to the door. Ellen
ng to try me, and Joe went with her. I

in the field and follow him around. Sometimes
he brought his grandfather, who always looked
closely at my legs.

"He's improving, Willie," Mr. Thoroughgood said. "I think we'll see a change for the
better by the spring."

The perfect rest, good food, soft turf, and
gentle exercise soon improved my condition and
spirits. I had a good constitution from my
mother, and I'd never been strained when
young, so I had a good chance of recovery.

During the winter my legs improved so
much that I began to feel young again. One
March day Mr. Thoroughgood decided to try
me in the light, four-wheel carriage. I was very
pleased. He and Willie drove me a few miles. My
legs weren't stiff now. I did the work with perfect ease.

"He's growing young, Willie. We must give
him a little gentle work now. By midsummer
he'll be as good as Ladybird. He has a beautiful
mouth and good paces. They can't be better."

"Oh, Grandpa, I'm so glad you bought
him!"

"So am I, my boy. He has you to thank
more than me. We must find a quiet, genteel
place for him, where he'll be valued."

CHAPTER 48

My Last Home

One day that summer, the groom cleaned and dressed me with such special care that I thought some new change must be at hand. He trimmed my fetlocks and legs, passed the tar brush over my hoofs, and even parted my forelock. The harness received an extra polish.

Willie seemed half-anxious, half-merry as he got into the light, two-wheel carriage with his grandfather.

"If the ladies like him," Mr. Thoroughgood said, "he'll suit them, and they'll suit him. It's worth a try."

About a mile from the village, we came to a pretty, low house with a lawn and shrubbery at the front and a drive up to the door. Willie rang the bell and asked for any of three sisters: Mary, Lavinia, or Ellen Blomefield.

While Willie stayed with me, Mr. Thoroughgood went into the house. In about ten minutes Mr. Thoroughgood returned, followed by the

three sisters. Lavinia wa[...] in a white shawl. She lea[...] lady with dark eyes and [...] very stately. They all can[...] asked questions.

Ellen took to me ve[...] has such a good face. I'[...]

Lavinia said, "I'd al[...] behind a horse who ha[...] again. If he did, I'd neve[...]

Mr. Thoroughgood [...] horses have had their k[...] their driver's carelessness [...] their own. From what I'[...] believe that to be true in [...] you can have him on trial [...] will see what he thinks of [...]

"You've always given [...] horses," Mary said. "Y[...] goes a long way with n[...] objection, we'll accept you[...] thanks."

It was arranged that I [...] next day.

In the morning a smar[...] came for me. At first he [...] when he saw my knee[...] Thoroughgood in a disap[...] surprised, sir, that you've r[...] ished horse to my ladies."

"H[...] Thorou[...] on trial [...] isn't as [...] him ba[...]

I w[...] fortabl[...]

Th[...] face w[...] the sta[...] same b[...] is now [...] careful [...] foreh[...] dle of [...] patch [...] do you [...] you?"

Jo[...] black [...] up to [...] I neve[...]

"[...] shoul[...] what s[...] You n[...] now. [...]

In[...] light [...] was g[...]

soon found that Ellen was a good driver. She seemed pleased with my paces. I heard Joe tell her about me. "I'm sure he's Squire Gordon's old Black Beauty."

When we returned, Mary and Lavinia came out to hear how I had behaved. Ellen told them what Joe had said. "I'll certainly write to Mrs. Gordon and tell her that her favorite horse has come to us. How pleased she'll be!" I was very happy to learn that Mrs. Gordon still was alive.

After this I was driven every day for a week or so. Because I appeared to be quite safe, Lavinia finally ventured out in the small carriage with me. The ladies decided to keep me and call me by my old name of Black Beauty.

I've now lived in this happy place a whole year. Joe is the best and kindest of grooms. My work is easy and pleasant. I feel my strength and spirits coming back. The other day Mr. Thoroughgood said to Joe, "At your place Black Beauty will live to be twenty, maybe older."

Willie always speaks to me when he can and treats me as his special friend.

My ladies have promised that I'll never be sold again, so I have nothing more to fear. My troubles are over.

Often in the morning, before I'm fully awake, I imagine that I'm still in the orchard at Birtwick, standing with my old friends under the apple trees.

About the Author

"If we see cruelty or some other wrong that we have the power to stop and we do nothing, we share in the guilt." In *Black Beauty* those words are spoken by the kindly gentleman Mr. Wright, who intervenes when he sees two horses being abused. His name pays tribute to John Wright, beloved grandfather of the book's author, Anna Sewell.

Anna was born in Yarmouth, England in 1820. Her parents, Mary and Isaac Sewell, were hardworking middle-class Quakers who valued kindness, charity, and equality.

Mary became an author of enormously popular stories that urged kindness to all creatures. Frogs "can feel," she wrote in one book, "and do not like pain more than you or I." Until Anna started attending school at age twelve, she was home-taught by Mary. Throughout her life Anna would remain exceptionally close to her mother. The two shared a love of animals and of literature. Later in life Anna would act as Mary's editor.

Isaac held many different jobs, including shop owner, traveling salesman, brewer, and banker. Mainly because he moved from job to job, the Sewells moved from place to place. When she was growing up, Anna lived in a number of villages in southern England, as well as major cities such as London and Bath.

Wherever the family went, they were in the company of animals, especially horses. One Sewell home was called Petlands. At various times the family kept chickens, cows, and pigs. Although the Sewells didn't own a horse until she was twenty-five, Anna rode and drove horses from childhood. She regularly talked to these horses and never used a whip. For years Anna had a pony, who may have inspired her character Merrylegs, Black Beauty's pony friend. Her brother Philip owned a black mare named Bessie, on whom Black Beauty may be based.

Even as a child, Anna spoke out against animal abuse. Once, a hunter shot a blackbird who fell, dead, onto the Sewells' property. When the man asked young Anna if he could take the dead bird, Anna angrily answered "No" and called him "cruel." A niece later would write of the adult Anna, "The sight of cruelty to animals . . . roused her indignation almost to fury, and wherever she was, or whoever she had to face,

About the Book

"**A**nimals can't tell us how they feel, but that doesn't mean that they suffer any less," a compassionate woman says in *Black Beauty: The Autobiography of a Horse* (1877). However, in *Black Beauty* animals *do* tell us how they feel. Horses speak to one another, and Black Beauty speaks directly to *us*. *Black Beauty* protests many ways in which humans inflict suffering on animals, from cropping dogs' ears to hunting hares. Primarily, though, the book gives voice to the suffering of horses.

Black Beauty and other horses are subjected to many encumbrances: saddles; bridles; "stiff, heavy" collars; irritating straps under their tails; iron shoes, which make their feet feel heavy and stiff; blinders, which prevent them from seeing anywhere other than straight ahead. Wearing a bit is "very bad," Black Beauty says. "A great piece of cold, hard steel as thick as a man's finger is pushed into your mouth, between your teeth, and over your tongue. The ends come out at the corners of your mouth and are held fast by straps over your head, under your throat, around your nose, and under your chin. There's no way that you can get rid of the nasty, hard thing." For a time Ginger is forced to wear *two* bits, which hurt her jaw and are so sharp that her tongue bleeds. With some owners Black Beauty and Ginger also wear checkreins, which cause discomfort or pain; strain a horse's mouth, neck, back, and legs; and can impair breathing.

Black Beauty laments the servitude of horses, who must "carry people on their back," drag vehicles, and go just as their rider or driver wishes. Horses "must always do what their master or mistress wishes," he says, "even though they may be very tired or hungry." They aren't allowed "any will of their own."

Many horses are ridden or driven harmfully fast. Having galloped as quickly as possible to and from a doctor's house, Black Beauty stands panting and sweating, with his legs shaking. Although in need of rest, Ginger is raced in a steeplechase. The overexertion strains her back and breathing. Pulling a cart with meat deliveries, a butcher's pony dashes from house to house. He returns to the butcher's shop "hot and exhausted. His head hung down, his sides heaved, and his legs trembled."

Horses struggle with heavy loads. Black Beauty describes two horses pulling a cart loaded with bricks: "Sweat streamed from their legs and flanks; their sides heaved; every muscle strained." Black Beauty himself hauls heavy carriages, carts, and cabs. At one point he pulls a cab so weighted with passengers and baggage that he collapses.

Whatever the weather, horses are forced to labor. They pull vehicles in intense heat and stand waiting, sometimes for hours, in soaking rain or freezing cold. Black Beauty sees Ginger—old, worn out, and emaciated—pulling a cab, as she does every day of the week. Her legs are wobbly and swollen, her joints "deformed from hard work." Her sides heave, and she repeatedly coughs. Her face is "full of suffering." Literally worked to death, she dies soon after.

Horses also suffer from human violence. Boys throw sticks and stones at colts, one of whom is "badly cut in the face, scarred for life." Other boys whip Merrylegs with sticks. Yet another boy whips and kicks a pony and punches him in the head. One man flogs Ginger and repeatedly digs his spurs into her sides. Another routinely hits her with a broom or pitchfork and, in one fit of rage, strikes her in the head with a whip. At times Black Beauty is whipped so severely that he bleeds.

Inadequate care and negligence cause further suffering. Many horses are underfed or fed an improper diet. Many are kept in uncomfortable stalls. In one stall Black Beauty has to stand on a slope—which is "very tiring." Another stall is depressingly dark, so dark that Black Beauty's eyes hurt whenever he emerges into daylight. One groom fails to keep Black Beauty's stall and feet clean. As a result, Black Beauty's feet become infected. Reckless driving causes accidents that seriously injure horses. In two such accidents a vehicle shaft rams into a horse's side or chest, tearing it open. Because a man leaves a lit pipe in a hayloft, a stable erupts into flames, and some horses burn to death.

Horses are social animals who naturally live in herds. Captive horses often suffer from loneliness. As soon as she is weaned, Ginger is taken from her mother. Black Beauty is permanently separated from his mother at age four. He comments, "People act as if horses have no family, but of course we do, even though we're often separated from our kin when one of us is sold." People also casually sever horse friendships. When Squire Gordon sells him, Black Beauty is separated from his close friend Merrylegs, whom he never sees again. At Lord Gerald's, Ginger tells Black Beauty, "They'll take you away soon. I'll lose the only friend I have." That's exactly what happens. "I didn't have a chance to really say goodbye to Ginger," Black Beauty recalls sadly. "We neighed to each other as I was led off, and she trotted anxiously along the hedge, calling to me as long as she could hear the sound of my feet." In his last home Black Beauty still longs for his "old friends."

In the end, the suffering of horses results from their being owned and controlled by humans. "However much I suffered, I did my best," Black Beauty says, because "humans have all the power. It was useless to resist." For the first three and a half years of his life, Black Beauty is largely free to accompany his mother and romp in a field with other colts. Then he is "broken" for human use. Like all the other horses in the book, Black Beauty lacks freedom. "It was dreadful to be shut up in a stall day after day instead of having liberty," Ginger says. "It's hard to have little liberty," Black Beauty agrees. Even when he receives exceptionally good treatment, Black Beauty desires freedom: "What more could I want? Liberty!"

The 1890 American edition of *Black Beauty* was subtitled "The Uncle Tom's Cabin of the Horse." Harriet Beecher Stowe's anti-slavery novel *Uncle Tom's Cabin* (1852) shows the suffering of those who are held as property and forced to serve a master or mistress. With regard to horses, *Black Beauty* does the same.